IT'S NOT ALWAYS
HAPPILY EVER AFTER

It's Not Always Happily Ever After

Lessons in Family Life from the Students of John Marshall and American Indian Heritage Schools

8 2 6
SEATTLE

With generous support from Barrie Trinkle
and 4Culture 4 CULTURE

TABLE OF CONTENTS

FOREWORD

Sherman Alexie

My late father was a serious reader, though he wasn't a reader of serious books.

I don't recall a Phillip Roth or William Faulkner on his shelves. He didn't own any Emily Dickinson or Walt Whitman. He didn't read about physics, economics, politics, or geography.

Instead, he read hundreds, maybe thousands, of westerns, spy novels, murder mysteries, and conspiracy tomes about JFK's assassination. Most of those books were pulpy gun fests. A few of them were well written and exciting. None of them were classic literature. But my father read all of them as seriously as any scholar has ever read William Blake.

My father read a book a day, every day, for decades.

And because I loved my father, I read with him. With books,

and through books, I followed him. After he finished a book, I would pick it up from his nightstand or shelf or car seat and read it, too.

I read a book a day, every day, for decades.

My father was not a great man. He was an ordinary man, a Coeur d'Alene Indian, who enjoyed a brief and shiny high school athletic career and then spent the rest of his life as a randomly employed reservation alcoholic.

He was, as they say, a disappointment. And yes, he often failed his family. We often felt poor and hopeless and ignored and afraid. We often felt invisible. I suspect that my father also felt like an invisible man.

But my father was also a kind and funny and loving man who tried to give his children a better life. I don't know if our reservation lives were ever easy, but my father certainly taught all of us how to be kind and funny and loving.

He taught us how to be generous with our time and spirit, even as we struggled in dire poverty.

He taught us how to tell jokes at the worst of times, because humor is an antiseptic that can heal the deepest of wounds.

He taught us how to read books.

More important, he taught us how to love books.

And because I loved reading books, I dreamed about being able to write books.

I dreamed about becoming a writer.

I wanted to be a storyteller.

And that's exactly what I have become.

My life is beautiful because of books.

It really is a simple formula.

It really is a direct path.

If you teach kids to read, then they have a better chance than kids who don't learn how to read.

If you teach kids how to love books, then they have a better chance at loving school than kids who don't love books.

If you teach kids how to tell stories, then they have a better chance at, well, at everything.

A better chance at love.

A better chance at life.

A better chance at work.

A better chance at play.

A better chance at hope.

Yes, books give us hope. Books teach us how to hope. Books are filled with hope. Books are hope.

The book you are holding is filled with hope. These are the stories of new writers. They are filled with laughter and tears and curses and howls at the moon.

Oh, these young people are not invisible.

Please, pay attention to these writers. Pay careful attention to their stories.

Please, listen.

Introduction

Optimism

We chose the theme of family for this book because we wanted a topic that would engage every student. We also knew that most of the students participating have pretty complicated family situations, although as one student told me, "It's not complicated. It's just the way it is."

While some of these stories are fiction, there is truth in all of them and lessons for those who pay attention.

Because this is the first year of operation for 826 Seattle, we might have opted for a more conventional group of students for our first publication. We could have chosen instead a high school full of students who had shared classes together for years and prid-

ed themselves on regular attendance. And, we would have if it were
not for Audra Gallegos, a teacher at John Marshall school. John
Marshall is a school of many programs: a teen mother program,
a re-entry program for students who have dropped out of school
temporarily, programs for special needs students, and programs for
students who simply arrive in the school district late in the scho-
lastic year. Audra discovered 826 Seattle in November 2005, about
three weeks after we opened our doors in Greenwood, a neighborhood that is easy to reach on the #48 bus from John Marshall over
by Green Lake. With her characteristic optimism, Audra put her
English class on the bus and brought them to 826 Seattle. She
reasoned that, if these students knew about 826 Seattle and its free
writing assistance programs, they would make a habit of coming to
us for help.

I'll never forget watching that surly pack of students disembark
from the bus and slump toward the front door of our storefront,
the Greenwood Space Travel Supply Co. They looked collectively
bored, with a tinge of irritation. Nevertheless, I asked them to
enter the writing center in the customary way—through the store's
automatic teleporter. Surprisingly, each agreed, and one by one
they entered the dark alcove and spun around through the black
curved door into our writing center.

"I know what you are all thinking," I said. "Here's another
middle-aged white woman do-gooder trying to find meaning in
her life by helping at-risk youth write. But you are wrong. I am
here out of selfishness."

Then I proceeded to tell them what I really believe—that their
generation must be smart and well-educated to clean up the messes
that my generation has rained on the world. I told them I believed
that young people in their situations, young people who haven't
had everything handed to them but have experienced life in an
important way, have a great deal to offer this country.

"But to offer it most effectively," I said, "you need to write well.
And I want that to happen, so my golden years will be spent in a
healthier country than we have now."

Then we wrote a poem together.

By the end of the meeting, 10 students had signed up to join
our Youth Advisory Board. One young woman, a poet, lingered

afterward to show me photos of her daughter and read me a few of her own poems.

But, none of them came back.

So, 826 Seattle went to them. Audra Gallegos said she could fold us into their regular school day, and we thought, "Ah, a captive audience!" At the time, it felt a little bit like those old Shirley Temple movies, or was it Spanky and Our Gang? "Let's put on a show!" or, in this case, "Let's publish a book!"

Sherman Alexie, who's on the 826 Seattle board of directors, agreed to be our sponsoring author. He inspired us to consider inviting another small alternative program to participate—the American Indian Heritage school. These students were especially interested in working on a joint project with such a renowned Native American author. The AIH students travelled to John Marshall for our tutoring sessions.

Audra let us take over her classes, encouraging other teachers to send their students to join us. She reserved the auditorium for Sherman Alexie's kick-off event, rode herd on the students' essays, called parents for permission slips, kept track of whose photos had been taken and whose author biographies was still missing. When we ran a little behind deadline, because three days a week for a month turned out not to be enough time for the project, she welcomed 826 Seattle tutors every day and for several class periods in a row. It wasn't even unusual for Audra to show up at 826 Seattle after hours (with her toddler daughter in tow) to give feedback on cover designs and deliver final essays on floppy disks.

Audra Gallegos is good in the way that many teachers are good. We are lucky to have teachers in our schools who care the way she cares.

I am very proud that 826 Seattle could spearhead the creation of the stories in this volume. I believe I speak for the many people who worked on this project when I say it has been enormously rewarding for all of us. Whether we were helping one student with a science fiction story or another with a difficult essay about his uncle, the process reminded us all that language is crucial—and that our young people hold much in their hearts that can benefit from the language of self-expression.

These stories, not always easy to read, reveal how life can be for many young people. In my opinion, they are much more the measure of a person than test scores and college entrance essays and acceptance into advanced placement classes. These stories reflect the wisdom that comes from living outside what many of us consider the conventional definition of family.

The students who created this book wrote many, many drafts, sitting for hours next to 826 Seattle tutors, jiggling, reworking, storming out of the room, walking back in, turning computers on, re-sharpening their pencils, and ultimately producing the poems, stories, and essays you hold in your hands right now. It was not always easy for the authors to turn what often started out as long journal entries into stories with a purpose for the public. It has taken hard work and patience and, in some cases, courage to write these stories.

I feel in my heart a great optimism for the future of these young people.

I am humbled by the honesty with which they have told their stories.

Teri Hein
Executive Director
826 Seattle
April 2006

IN MY **DREAM** I WAS IN MY **OLD APARTMENT** WHERE I LIVED WITH MY **GRANDMA** AND **GRANDPA**, BUT THE HOUSE WAS NOW **DARK** AND **SPOOKY**. I WAS LOOKING AROUND, TRYING TO **FIGURE OUT** WHAT HAPPENED, WHEN SOMETHING **WALKED** BY ME. THEN MY **GRANDPA APPEARED**, STARING AT ME WITH A **SERIOUS** LOOK. HE **SAID**, "YOU **BETTER CHANGE** YOUR WAYS, **BOY**," AND THEN **DISAPPEARED**.

-DEVONTE PARSONS

DEVONTE'S UNTOLD STORY

Devonte Parsons

My grandma used to be a housekeeper for the movie star Jimmy Durante back in her early ages. She also used to work in Hollywood with some other famous stars. About twenty-five years ago my grandma moved to Seattle from California.

When I was born I lived with my mom in Texas. My dad died before I was born so I never had the chance to see him. The only people that did were my older brother and my mom. My mom used to like partying when she was young and I used to get babysat by different people. My grandma did not like that so she came all the way from Seattle to pick me up, and my grandma is nice, so that's the reason I think she's my idol. When I was born, my grandma was the first person to hold me.

When I was little my grandpa took me everywhere with him. I

remember him taking me to the baseball game, specifically, because that was the last place I went with him before he died. He died at the train station getting ready to go to his friend's house. I was little, so when my grandma told me, I did not know what was going on. I asked her every day when he was going to come back home. It took me a few months to realize he wasn't.

When I was eleven I found out about my dad. He was shot and killed while walking down the street in Texas. I found a picture of him and my mom and hung it up in my room. I was scared to ask my mom what happened because she might start crying. My uncle told me part of the story. He said that my dad was walking down the street when it happened, and my uncle did not know who it was at the time. The person that killed him eventually went to jail and was killed in there. I'm trying to get information from different sources and piece the puzzle together.

I first started getting in trouble at school when I was in third grade. I think my grandma was most upset when I got expelled from Washington Middle School because I was doing so well at first, but then I fell off. I don't exactly know what I was expelled for, but I think it was because a lot of minor things built up on me and they got tired of it. I was doing un-smart things like disrupting the class by messing with people, or blurting answers out loud, and making beats with my hands.

Before I got expelled we had a meeting to decide what the punishment was going to be. Everybody that got involved with me at Washington was there, and so was my grandma. As far as I know they had already made the decision but just held the meeting to tell me what it was. As I sat at that big round table with all eyes on me, I felt very uncomfortable, as if I were on stage with millions of people waiting for me to say something. After sitting there for a while talking about why I do the things I do, they told me their decision. Tears of anger rolled from my eyes, but I did not cry, yell, or throw anything. I just got up, took it like a man, and left. I could tell in my grandma's eyes that she was disappointed. The night before, she had cried because she did not know what to do with me.

It was like the trouble I got into grew with me. When I was in sixth grade I was getting detention and suspended. When I got to seventh grade I got suspended and emergency expelled three times. I also had a few police run-ins outside of school.

One time, my friends and I decided to go to the mall. We saw a tip jar full of money in Jamba Juice. My friends ran in and grabbed some money and I didn't want to be left out, so I grabbed some, too. After that we ran around the mall and got kicked out with the police called on us. We were waiting for the bus by this gas station and messing with the gas, so they called the police, too. We finally caught the bus and were on our way home when two cop cars pulled up and told the bus to stop, then took us out. As we were sitting down in handcuffs outside the bus stop a lot of things were going through my mind: my grandma, my mom, and my future. The police were talking to us while another one called my grandma. I thought I was going to juvenile for sure, but they decided to let it go and put it on my non-permanent record. One of my friends and I went home, but the other was a runaway and had to go to the Spruce Street Crisis Residential Center. That night my grandma was real disappointed in me, but I was too shocked by this encounter with the police to notice.

After being grounded for a month I decided to change and stop stealing and committing crimes. My grandma was the one who inspired me to stop getting into trouble, but a dream I had stopped me from doing it completely. In my dream I was in my old apartment where I lived with my grandma and grandpa, but the house was now dark and spooky. I was looking around, trying to figure out what happened, when something walked by me. I ran back to my room and sat there. I started hearing barking from inside the house. It wasn't a regular bark but it was more of a disturbing, sad bark. I walked in the living room and saw my dog that had died a couple years before. Then my grandpa appeared, staring at me with a serious look. He said, "You better change your ways, boy," and then disappeared.

I woke up so scared I was sweating. I told my grandma and she said that might have been a sign, so listen to him. The weird thing about it is she said she had a dream about him the same night in the same place. I was rattled but I still listened. I started doing better in school for a while until I got angry with a kid for trying to yell at me. I blew out, and started throwing things and cursing. I got emergency expelled for that.

I'm now in eighth grade. I have been trying my best to do well in school, and I haven't had that dream at all. But still to this day when I have a slipup I try to think about my grandma and grandpa and how they would feel about what I am doing.

*Thirteen-year -old **Devonte Parsons** would like you to know that he doesn't change depending on who he's around—he's the same outgoing, cool, smart person. His goals are to graduate from college, expand his vocabulary, and be a rapper. He enjoyed the 826 Seattle project and "the chance to have my story in a book and tell about my life and growing up."*

STILL, HEARING THE RUSTLE OF FOOTSTEPS behind them, MY DAD and uncle WEREN'T AFRAID. They KNEW who this ANIMAL was. DAD said it was their FATHER PROTECTING them as they were WALKING HOME.

-MARISA D. LOPEZ

SEEDS

Marisa D. Lopez

I am half Indian, three-eighths Caucasian, and one-eighth Asiatic/
Austro-Hungarian and Gypsy. I educated myself about the
many cultures I am descended from, and my pride comes from
many places. One place I know well is my father's stories from his
people. I was curious about where I came from. I guess all kids
are. For me, it was important to understand how they did things
back then. Daddy's stories really taught me about the similarities
between people, and that, although times may have changed,
people haven't.

Some stories Daddy told me were of his family when he was a
kid, growing up in the Indian village of Ocoronee. I always liked
hearing his stories about my grandfather, who was a wise man
and healer, a warrior of his clan, the Acalua. They speak the same

language as the Yaqui, but have the same religious customs as the Chiricahua and Nednhi Apache of Sonora and Sinaloa, Mexico.

The story of the Rain Dance was a story that I always loved to hear my dad tell. When he was six years old, there was no rain for many months, so his people could not grow corn. The tribe decided to get together and have dances and prayers. Indian dancing can go on for days on end. It's always a prayer to Yusen to bless the people with rain, to grow food and become healthy and strong. Dances always got my dad and all the other little kids excited. Elders would dance in the inner circle, while the rest of the tribe danced in a larger outer circle. The circle has significance to my father's people—it symbolizes continuity. Daddy said that whenever somebody in the outer circle got tired, another would take his or her place in the circle. My father remembers that the elders sang and danced without ever leaving the inner circle. I found that amazing.

Grandfather led the prayers during the Rain Dance as the drum and shakers kept a steady rhythm. For three days, not a cloud was in the sky, and the hot sun beat down. The third day, a dark cloud appeared overhead, and the people danced, sang and prayed harder and faster than before. Daddy jumped around with the other kids, moving his legs faster and faster to the beat. Not long after, the cloud moved above the dancers. They felt a strong power around them and it began raining hard. The people thanked the creator, Yusen, and the crops grew. I love that story because of the way my dad uses his sense of humor to tell it.

For the most part, his life was very country-hickish, even for an Indian. He rode horses and worked on a little farm near his family's house. One evening, my dad and his brother were walking a horse with a load of corn plants, heading home for the night. My dad's brother had a hard time walking, as he was born with a limp. They walked the horse up a steep, rocky hill, and after they got to the top, they sat down to rest. My dad stupidly tied the horse's lead rope around his ankle. The two were standing around drinking some water when a herd of wild horses ran past the bottom of the hill. The herd must have had at least four females, and my dad's horse happened to be a stallion. Well, when that stallion saw those pretty, young mares, he dug his four hooves into the dirt and ran down that hill like a rocket. My dad was dragged down the hill, his pants ripped, bleeding from his legs and bottom and yelling to his brother to help him get the rope off his ankle. His brother ran as fast as he could to catch the stallion, but Dad was already at the bottom of the hill in a bunch of mesquite bushes, screaming like a girl. My uncle had to carefully pick my dad out of the bushes. Dad ended up having my three aunts picking mesquite pricklies out of his butt. Everybody in the village laughed at him. Normally I'd laugh at a story like this, but my dad must have been really sore, so I actually felt sorry for him.

When he told me a short story of an animal following them home in the dark, it put a smile on my face. My grandfather told my dad and his brother, who were twelve and sixteen years old at the time, that they should be careful when walking in the dark. One night he told his sons that they shouldn't go out that night because it was dangerous and they might get themselves into trouble—or worse.

My dad and uncle didn't listen. It was dark before they got even halfway home, and they were beginning to understand why they shouldn't have gone out in the evening, even though the moon was very bright and they could see the path ahead. They began to feel a strange presence behind them as they were walking. Still, hearing the rustle of footsteps behind them, my dad and uncle weren't afraid. They knew who this animal was. Dad said it was their father protecting them as they were walking home.

Whatever you may believe about these stories, the message is one of togetherness of people. The seed that is watered through prayer and dedication can grow into something beautiful. Protection and guidance of young people, teaching them the old ways of doing things no matter where your family is from, are important. You will share stories with your own children. This is what I have learned.

*Eighteen-year-old **Marisa D.
Lopez** is Apache, Lakota, Eastern
Cherokee, and German. Her
teachers Boo, Ms. Colby, and
Strash have all inspired her to go
to college, where she hopes to study
music and fine arts. This project
was a chance for her to "tell the
stories of my father's people and
tell others that it's never too late to
learn about where you come from."
When she's not writing, Marisa
plays classical guitar, studies politics
and social issues, and tries to learn
from people of other cultures.*

I WENT TO JUVIE FOR

THE FIRST TIME, GOT ON

PROBATION, RAN AWAY,

STARTED SMOKING

CIGARETTES AND WEED. I WAS

DOING 252 MPH DOWN

A DANGEROUS RECKLESS

ROAD. 252 MEANS

2 MUCH

5 TIMES

2 FAST.

-BRENDA MCMILLIN

I Can Do Bad By Myself

Brenda McMillin

Here I was, bad, hardheaded, thirteen going on twenty-one. Spitfire in my heart and cold defiance in my eyes, ready to take on the world one authority figure at a time. I was petite with a spry little budding figure and the muscles of a young bodybuilder. My daddy made me do sets of pushups every time I misbehaved, which was ninety percent of the time. I could probably do about 200 pushups an hour, that's how strong I was. Pushups or no, I was still bad and couldn't no one tell me nuthin. I couldn't stand my momma. Now that I think back on what we went through, I believe that most of our problems derived from lack of communication.

I remember the year 2000-2001 well. I tried to block it out of my memory, but no matter what, I will never forget that year. I had messed up bad in seventh grade. I was constantly suspended or getting into trouble at school. I went to juvie for the first time, got on probation, ran away, started smoking cigarettes and weed. I was doing 252 mph down a dangerous reckless road. 252 means 2 much 5 times 2 fast.

That summer I decided that I didn't want to follow the rules at home, and I went to stay at various youth shelters and group homes throughout Seattle. My first group home was on Aurora. I went to an interagency school downtown even after being warned about how bad the school was. It was my first taste of street life, and at fourteen I thought it was heaven.

I almost completely withdrew from my family, only talking to them when I saw them at random court dates and to get their consent for some of my placements. The street kids who were trying successfully to turn me out were now my family. Being turned out means getting into things like shoplifting, drugs, and sex. It's a scary path to travel, but on the way you learn life lessons that aren't to be learned anywhere else. Trust is like a gift you give and only those who truly love and respect you give a gift in return.

The following school year I went back home. I'd worn out my welcome everywhere, but I realized how young I was and that school was important to me. So I went back to school in my neighborhood, but basically followed the same patterns I had the year before. It seemed my parents never failed to rub in my face how screwed up I was, and I was uncomfortable and resentful, which only added fuel to the fire. I continued going to juvie and seeing an array of counselors and psychiatrists. Finally, after my fourth D.V.—domestic violence—assault on my mom, I was sent away to a behavior rehab facility for eleven months. When I got out, I was sixteen and still had a bad attitude, with a mindset of superior invincibility. That attitude slowly floated away after I kept getting in trouble. My family and I still weren't getting along because I had refused to return home after I was released from the behavior rehab facility.

So again I found I had to depend on myself, but by now I was getting used to it. I knew now how it was going to be, so I began to take more independent strides in life. Recently I have been getting myself together and focusing on making it on my own.

My mom still sometimes tries to control me even though I don't live with her, but we have been getting along more now that I've gotten older and more mature. Maybe she sees how much I have grown emotionally and figures that I can do good by myself. Or maybe she sees me as an adult now, responsible for my own actions, who can do perfectly bad by myself.

As for me, well, I know I can do bad by myself, but it's funny—I think I'm warming up to the idea of doing good by myself.

*Eighteen-year-old **Brenda McMillin's** goal is to be independent and self-sufficient. For now she enjoys shopping, reading, and hanging out with friends. She liked the 826 Seattle project and is inspired by herself.*

...HAPPILY EVER AFTER

17

WHO IS THIS FAMILY
FROM WHICH HE
COMES?

-TYSON ALEXANDER WATSON

QUESTIONS

Tyson Alexander Watson

QUESTIONS I

You were the one who brought me to this world.
Why weren't you the one to walk me through it?

I don't understand it all.
Why did you let me be taken from you?
   Did you want that?
   Did you need that?
Were you forced to make this choice?
These are the things I need to know.

Why would you have a child at such a young age?

Why couldn't you wait?
Why couldn't you think?

I don't understand it all.
Why did you let me be taken from you?
  Did you want that?
  Did you need that?
Were you forced to make this choice?
These are the things I need to know.

Did this child do something that you didn't like?
What could this little boy have done so wrong?
What could he have done to receive your love?

I don't understand it all.
Why did you let me be taken from you?
  Did you want that?
  Did you need that?
Were you forced to make this choice?
These are the things I need to know.

Have you no reason to care?
  Did you then?
  Do you now?

I don't understand it all.
Why did you let me be taken from you?
  Did you want that?
  Did you need that?
Were you forced to make this choice?
These are the things I need to know.

What could this child have done to earn a name?
What could he have done to have learned yours?
Who is this family from which he comes?

I don't understand it all.
Why did you let me be taken from you?

Did you want that?
Did you need that?
Were you forced to make this choice?
These are the things I need to know.

That child was me.
That child felt pain.
That child wanted to know your name, wanted—needed—a
   name from you.
That child needed you, but you were not there.

You will never know me as your son.
You will never know me as someone that you could have loved.
You will never know me as someone that could have loved you.
You will never know the strength of my hand in yours walking
   together.

My name is Tyson.
I walk alone.

QUESTIONS 2

What is the duty of a father?
Is he supposed to be there when his son is born?
Is he supposed to give his son a name?
Is he supposed to comfort his son in times of need?

What is the duty of a father?
Should he read his son stories before bed? And then stay at his
   bedside until he falls asleep?
Should he wake his son in the morning and teach him to make
   pancakes?
Should he take him out on his boat and teach him to fish?

What is the duty of a father?
Should he take him on a hunting trip?
Should he take him to a gun range and teach him to shoot?
What are the things that a father should do with his son?

Are there specific guidelines to follow?
Is there a "father figure" book for dads that have no idea
how to be one?
Should there be?

What is the duty of a father?

*"My imagination." This is what sixteen-year-old **Tyson Alexander Watson** likes most about himself. Maybe he gets some of it from his mom, a writer who inspires him. Tyson's own goal is to become a successful lawyer. Until then he enjoys playing video games, hanging out with friends, and playing with his pit bull, Chance.*

I AM QUITE PROUD OF MY
INDEPENDENT SPIRIT.
I DRESS THE WAY I WANT,
I ACT THE WAY I WANT, I
REACH THE GOALS I SET.

-ZAK BRINLEE

WITHOUT THE REFRIGERATOR PICTURES

Zak Brinlee

My name is Zak. I am seventeen years old. I am not what some would call "normal looking." I have long black hair, many facial piercings, and large holes in my ears. I am quite proud of my independent spirit. I dress the way I want, I act the way I want, I reach the goals I set.

I attend John Marshall High School in Seattle, Washington, as a junior. I plan to graduate early and go on to have my own business. I am the first to admit I wasn't always the best in school. I have failed some classes and others I skipped. I was taught to be polite, say please and thank you, and always open doors for ladies. I am proud of how I turned out as a person: smart, polite, kind, caring, and humorous. I am most proud of my thirst for knowledge. In my life I have been successful in staying absolutely drug-free, meaning I have never tried a drug once. I have held many jobs, from building construction to working in a private lounge. I drive my dream car, a Mercedes Benz 190E, that I am very proud to own due to a summer of two jobs and hard work.

Many people might think that I came from a "good" traditional home because of how I've turned out. That's not really true. In fact, in some ways, my upbringing has been difficult. I grew up in a mostly single-parent home with my mother and, for a few early years, my brother Tim. I never felt much support from my mother. She never made me feel that the sky was the limit. My mom was a bit overprotective as well; I never got to attend school dances or birthday parties. For no apparent reason, my mom never trusted me, and would constantly call the house when she knew I should be home from school.

I've never really understood her much. To get a better idea of her, it would help if you knew where she came from. My mother did not come to America until she was six years old. She came from Mexico with her mother and father and six brothers and sisters. She did not know English, so she had to learn by being around English-speaking people. As a family they moved a lot, traveling with migrant camps, never really making much money. The family finally settled in the outskirts of Salem, Oregon. In the high school there she met my father. They dated until they both graduated, and then married. After that things did not go well for our small family. My parents constantly fought. They had four boys, and managed to stay together for twenty years. My mother left my father when I was seven years old; she took my two older brothers of eleven and twelve, and me. I still don't know why she left.

My mother's house, where I live now, is not the traditional family home. There are not a lot of pictures of my brothers and me, or family portraits. The refrigerator is not covered with school grade reports or awards. I had many good report cards and a few awards that I was quite proud of, but I never felt they were praised or even noticed.

I remember a time when my friend Damien came over when my mom was home. Damien is a regular kind of guy. He has double lip piercings and each ear pierced many times, with big gouges in each ear. He was very polite and kind. He didn't use any foul language or anything that my mom would find rude or offensive. He even helped me mow the lawn for my mom and take out the trash. Once he left for the day, my mom told me she never wanted him at the house again. When I asked why, she said that Damien scared her. I asked her how could she say that when he was so nice and polite. She just said he scared her, and she didn't like him. In my mom's view, people with unnatural hair color (green, red, orange, purple, pink, etc.) have "identity problems," meaning they don't know who they are or where they come from, and are confused.

I am the way I am because my mom, in her own ironic way, motivated me to be my own person. She has pushed me to be better, even when I thought I was good enough. She has inspired me to excel by making me feel that I could be better than she thinks. Would I be the way I am, a way I am proud of, if she had been more supportive? I'd have to say no.

Seventeen-year-old **Zak Brinlee** *does not live with his mother, and they don't always get along, but they are on speaking terms. Zak hopes to one day own his own business. People who make it on their own inspire him, and his hobbies include working, his car, and his friends.*

Her FATHER never BOTHERED with BASEMENTS, AND her MOTHER was too DISGUSTED by the DUST and COBWEBS. Emily LIKED it, the DARKNESS, the sound of BUGS SCATTERING around, and the EERIE GLOW that ALWAYS came from the CORNER.

-Rachel V. Hammer

EMILY

Rachel V. Hammer

"Emily is such a strange child," Emily Vanderzon's mother said to the school principal. The principal, Mr. Hardter, stood up nodding.

"True, Emily is strange," Mr. Hardter muttered, sounding tired, "but that is no excuse for her behavior. I'm sorry to have so many bad things to say about your daughter, Mrs. Vanderzon, but Emily talks out of turn, doesn't listen to the teacher, absolutely refuses to do group work, and has no regard for her grades. I would really appreciate it if you could have a talk with her, Mrs. Vanderzon."

"Don't worry, I will," Mrs. Vanderzon said, gathering her purse and jacket.

A fourteen-year-old girl with long black hair and emerald green eyes looked up and stuck her tongue out as Mrs. Vanderzon entered the waiting area of the school office. "Hi, Mom," Emily said, jumping up.

Mrs. Vanderzon sighed. "Get in the car, Emily. We have to have yet another chat about school."

Emily feigned a look of innocence, but she really felt quite proud. "I WILL make Mom realize I'm not some perfect little lady that she can buy obedience from! I'm only ME!" she thought, slamming the door shut. This earned a dark scowl from her mother.

"Sure you will…" a low, mocking voice murmured in her mind. The voice belonged to none other than Grimes, one of her "pets." Grimes was a strange demon that had lived in her family's mansion since before even her great-great grandmother had been born. Grimes wasn't the only one, though. The Vanderzons' mansion was infested with demons. But only Emily had ever met them. To her, they were more like a family than her real parents.

* * *

Emily bolted up the stairs to her room as soon as she was home, completely ignoring her mother's calls and screaming "SUGAR!" at the top of her lungs, for no reason at all. She turned on the TV and flopped down on the bed. An unusual catlike creature with a long neck and huge ears appeared next to her. If it weren't for the fact that its body was made of smoke, it would have looked at least a little normal. "Hey, Grimey," Emily grinned.

Grimes scowled. "Why must you ALWAYS call me that?"

"I want to. Where are Asdelette and Nytro?"

"Asdelette is in the kitchen, as usual, and since when do I ever know where Nytro is?"

"Then where's Abella? Maybe she'll play Monopoly with me or something."

"Since when do you want to be around Abella? She's more annoying than those used car advertisers. There's something wrong with you, isn't there? Start talking, little girl," Grimes said, tilting his head to the side. "You're acting whinier than usual, too."

Emily glowered at him and stuck her tongue out. Finally she sighed. "Fine," she muttered. "If you must know, I've been trying for two years to get Mom to stop trying to make me perfect, and she just doesn't get it. Now I have to suffer through another one of her long-winded lectures about my well-being and how I should grow up to be her perfect little lady. She claims I'm allergic to animals, but it's just an excuse so she doesn't have to put up with them. If Mom had less money she'd stop being so ignorant of other things around her, like how I so obviously hate my school. And I'm so sick of Dad always being gone. He's the only person who likes to have fun in my family. And one day you demons are going to leave me too!"

Emily rolled over and lay on her stomach, frowning into the pillow. Grimes jumped up on the bed and curled up on her back.

"Well, Emily, there is a way to... change a few things..."

"Really? How?" Emily asked, sitting up. Grimes jumped off of her and sat on the bed.

"Simple," he replied. "Just call on Zin Generin. He can give you whatever life you want. But be careful, he likes to play some rather twisted games."

"I'll be careful. How do I call him?"

"Let's go to the portal room." Grimes jumped off the bed and trotted off. Emily followed him, smiling.

* * *

The portal room was really just the large basement of the house. Even though it was known as the portal room, you couldn't see anything special, just a mirror. The mirror looked rather normal, but Emily knew better than to believe that anymore. It didn't matter, though, since she was the only one who had ever been down here. Her father never bothered with basements, and her mother was too disgusted by the dust and cobwebs. Emily liked it—the darkness, the sound of bugs scattering around, and the eerie glow that always came from the corner. Even Grimes couldn't explain what it was, so he and Emily just stayed away from it. Grimes walked up to the mirror and sat down. Emily stood in front of it, ignoring the odd, spiderlike monstrosity that had suddenly appeared on the ceiling. She was too used to the creature, known as Xefon, to be afraid of or startled by him. "Well, Emily, do the honors. You know how." Emily nodded, not at all nervous. Even though most monsters came through on their own, Emily had still called many of them out of their own world and into hers.

* * *

BRRRRIIIIIIING!!!!

"Emily Vanderzon! Get in here, class has already started!" called Mr. Tallweed, Emily's second-period math teacher.

"When I'm ready!" Emily called back, putting her backpack in her locker and lazily pulling out her art book and a couple of Sharpies. "Stay here, okay, Kasumi?" she whispered to what looked like a little white mouse, except for its forked tongue and neon green eyes. Kasumi hissed and crawled into Emily's pack. Emily spun around and walked into class, ignoring Mr. Tallweed's stern gaze.

"Now that Ms. Vanderzon has joined us, let's begin," Mr. Tallweed grumbled.

"Hey!" Emily snapped. "My name's EMILY! Get that through your head, guy. Not Ms. Vanderzon, EM-IL-Y. Jeez! How hard is it to remember THAT?!" Emily sat back in her seat, pleased with the evil glare delivered by the teacher. Considering how strict and harsh Mr. Tallweed was, Emily was sure that causing him problems was a good deed. At least it would help in her goal of "Making Mom realize I'm not her little doll." A couple other students were trying not to laugh.

"Get your book out, Emily Vanderzon, and turn to page 68. Do problems number 5 through number 26. It's a review. The rest of you, same page, same problems. No talking!"

Emily made a disgusting face at Mr. Tallweed before finally getting to work.

"Wow! Emily, that was SOOO amazing! The way you stood up to Tallweed!" gushed a tall girl with huge gray eyes and frizzy red hair. Emily growled, not liking the girl, Cindy, at all. She was also getting sick of Cindy always following her around after math class. It was even beginning to drive her crazy. "But," Emily thought, smirking, "if I can get her to go cry to a teacher about how mean I'm being, then maybe Mom will receive yet another little call about her perfect daughter..."

"Go away, Cindy. I do things like that every day. And if I'm so amazing, then start worshipping me in silence."

"But, Emily! It was the best thing I've ever seen…" Cindy was cut off as Emily snarled, "Shut up, already! Didn't you hear what I just said? Why can't you go annoy the cheerleaders or the nurse? Scat, brat!" Emily turned and ran off toward her next class, science. At least she liked this class, especially since they were doing experiments with chemicals. Emily liked to watch things go "POOF" when someone made a mistake. "Only a few more hours to go… and, unfortunately, I don't think I was evil enough. Oh well, better luck next time," she thought to herself.

* * *

Emily ran upstairs as soon as she got home. Her mother wouldn't be home for another forty-five minutes. As she entered her room, she saw the demon sitting on her bed. He was rather human, but had large, pointed, batlike ears, and clouded gray eyes. His skin was a pale grayish green color, and his white hair fell below his back. Last but not least, there was a pair of large, bony wings folded behind him. He was no doubt one of the Hildan demons.

"Are you Zin Genesis?" she asked, putting her pack down on the floor.

"Zin Generin," he corrected in a soft, whisperlike voice. "I take it you're Emily, judging by what the Safan demon told me."

Emily nodded. Then blinked. "Uhhhh… what's a Safan demon?"

Grimes suddenly appeared, saying, "Me, Emily. I thought I told you that?"

"Probably. Just didn't remember," Emily replied, shrugging. She turned to Zin Generin. "So," she started, "how in the world can you help me? And no tricks!" Zin stood up.

"I've already dealt with it. Your friend Grimes told me about you, and don't worry. I owe him a favor, so I won't cause you any problems. Basically, your father has been fired, and your mother's main bank account was deleted. You won't be rich anymore so you can finally begin to experience middle-class life like you want. You can act more like yourself in a school where it's not about who buys the most expensive stuff. You'll have to move, but your father will spend more time with you, and your mother will have to stop treating you like some little trophy rich girl, and more like a regular teenager," Zin explained.

Emily thought for a moment, before replying, "I like it. How long will all this take?"

"You'll have a new life by next week." With that, Zin left.

* * *

"I'm sorry, but this house just isn't right," Mrs. Vanderzon said arrogantly as the salesman asked how she liked it. Emily usually would've been embarrassed by how her mother was acting, but now, sitting in the back of a rental car, she was thinking more about her demon friends in the mansion. Three days, and she already felt like they'd left her centuries ago, only worse. She still hadn't gotten used to Grimes not being there to tell her what to do and sometimes make her laugh, and of course, she missed creepy little Kasumi being there as a tiny companion, which also made her feel very lonely. Was the loss of her friends the trick that Zin might've played, even though he promised not to? Grimes had said to be careful, but she hadn't asked why. Grimes had been the one to explain the situation.

Emily quickly pulled herself away from her thoughts as Mrs. Vanderzon slammed the driver side door shut. "Well, Emily, another house not worth looking at. I really wish your father would hurry up and get here," she added angrily. Emily ignored her, and reached down to grab a magazine with a fancy home on the front. "Mom must have forgotten about this one," she thought. She flipped it open to a random page, and began glancing over it.

"...And then the salesman said that he thought I wasn't..." Emily tuned out her mother's blabber and glanced out the window. She'd pored through the entire magazine twice and hadn't found anything nice. Growling, she flipped to yet another random page, only to see the house she'd been hoping to find. "Strange," she thought. "This house wasn't in here before, was it?" She kept looking at the little ad for the small, two-story white and green

house. A nice yard with a white fence around it, and a little creek
behind the house. "Hey, Mom!" she said, waving the magazine in
her face. "Let's check this one out!" Mrs. Vanderzon braked and
looked at the ad.

"All right, all right, Emily," she replied. "We'll look at it. It's
nearby, too."

Emily threw herself back in her seat happily as Mrs. Vanderzon
started driving again.

"Finally!! Mom had BETTER like this one," Emily thought.
She was already sick of hotels and driving, especially since the car
was beginning to smell like cheese. Of course, that was probably
her fault for spreading nacho cheese under the seat. She couldn't
wait to find a nice house. Not to mention the fact that she'd be able
to go to a normal school, not one for rich kids only. That would
be a relief. "Things are finally going how I want them to. Took
the world long enough!" she thought, watching out the window.
"Anyways, I'll just annoy Mom to death if she decides not to take
the house."

* * *

Two weeks later, Emily had settled into her new town and
small, cozy home. She liked her new school much better, and, like
Zin promised, Mr. Vanderzon stayed home more. Both her parents had good, well-paying jobs, and were getting used to the new
arrangements. And to make things even better, three demons had
been granted permission to stay with her. It meant that they could
never return to their world again, but they all had chosen on their
own. Grimes, Kasumi, and a young Hildan demon named Mitaray.
Like Zin had promised, there were no horrible tricks.

For once, things seemed to be looking up. Except for…

"Emily! Homework!"

Emily just smiled innocently at Grimes and put her video game
on pause. "Yeah. What about it, Grimey?" she asked sweetly.

Grimes glared. "You have two days left to finish a five-page
book report. What do you have so far?"

"Sheesh. You're worse than Mom. But don't worry, Grimey! I've
thought of the first two words for the title. I'll do the rest tomor-

row," Emily laughed.

Grimes just stared at her like she was crazy, then shook his head. "Suit yourself... Oh, and Mitaray wants to go outside again."

Emily nodded to show she heard him.

Mitaray was a young Hildan that Emily had met on her last day in the mansion. He was a nine-year-old orphan and completely mute. Unlike Grimes and Kasumi who had abandoned their world because they wanted to stay with Emily as companions, Mitaray had clung to her until she said he could come with her too. Emily had soon learned that he was actually afraid of the demon world. She still didn't know why, but decided she would figure it out on her own. Now he was like a little brother to her, and better yet, he didn't get in the way at all. He hid from Mr. and Mrs. Vanderzon like he had been told, and he liked to sleep under her bed because it was so small and dark. He also liked to play a lot. One of his favorite games was hide-and-seek.

* * *

Emily sighed as she worked in her Language Arts book, sitting in the overly hot classroom. It didn't help that someone was wearing so much perfume it felt like she was close to suffocating. She might've liked this school much better than her last one, but this class was too horrible for its own good. "And the teacher is even worse!" Emily mentally growled. "If he didn't drone on and on and on in that awful voice of his, at least it might be a LITTLE better!" She dropped her head on her desk. "Someone, PLEASE make the last twenty minutes with this guy be over...!" Sometimes it was really hard to keep up her good attitude, but she was still trying.

* * *

"WHEEEEEEEEEEE!!!!!" Emily cheered, riding down the stairs in her house on a sled. It was a Wednesday, but she didn't have to go to school.

"EMILY!!" Mrs. Vanderzon screeched. "Put that thing upstairs this instant!! Just because I let you miss school for your dentist appointment does NOT mean you can tear apart the house!"

"Fine, be that way," Emily retorted and ran upstairs, throwing the sled in her closet. The weatherman had forecasted snow within the next week, so Emily had been gearing up.

Grimes was lying on her bed, watching her with a look that clearly said "You need help." "How did your report go?" he asked, standing and stretching.

"Dunno. Ms. Albing didn't say anything."

Emily flopped down on her bed laughing.

"You're sure happy today. Why? I know nothing special happened, and I know you utterly hate dentists. Did Mitaray or Kasumi screw with your head last night or something?"

"Jeez, Grimey. Am I not allowed to be in a good mood?" Grimes just watched her. Emily rolled her eyes. "I finally got the life I've wanted since I was six… with a few demons added in, but whatever… Now, I can finally grow up normally!" Emily collapsed on the floor, grinning.

"And?" Grimes asked.

"Dad's taking me to the fair on Saturday. I'm gonna have the time of my life getting sick on the roller coaster," she replied.

Grimes just rolled his eyes and went back to sleep, leaving Emily to be her weird self.

"I'm from Alaska, and I like classic rock." Fifteen-year-old **Rachel V. Hammer** *would like you to know this about her. Her goal is to become a pilot, and she is inspired by J.K. Rowling and her dad. She also enjoys video games, CG, programming, mechanics, and writing.*

ONE OF THE **HARDER**

POINTS OF **PARENTING**

IS **KNOWING** THAT YOUR

KIDS ARE GOING TO **MAKE**

THEIR **OWN DECISIONS.**

MAKING OUR OWN

DECISIONS IS WHAT **LETS**

US KNOW WE CAN **TRUST**

OUR OWN **INSTINCTS,**

WHICH IN MY **OPINION** IS

CRUCIAL TO **LIVING** A **LIFE**

YOU LOVE AND **LOVING**

THE **LIFE YOU LIVE.**

- J.R.

PARENTING MY PARENTS

J. R.

A beautiful mistake. My mom was pregnant before my parents got married. In all likelihood it is the reason they got married, so just like fifty percent of all marriages in the US, they got a divorce when I was three. This disrupted my emotional status in a big way because I started to be very destructive and angry. If my parents would have been like some parents and punished me for my "bad" behavior, then I probably would have gotten worse and never dealt with those problems. Being closed minded or thinking with limits can be destructive in any area but especially parenting. Instead they found other ways for me to work out my aggression.

Someone once told me that life is about finding out who you are and then being that person. Your personality is mostly made up by your decisions and how you feel about your decisions.

Parents control their kids' environments as much as they can as their children grow up, and one of the harder points of parenting is knowing that your kids are going to make their own decisions. Making our own decisions is what lets us know we can trust our own instincts, which in my opinion is crucial to living a life you love and loving the life you live.

Too many people don't think for themselves. They assume that everyone else is doing it so why shouldn't they. Sometimes the substance in question is not E. Sometimes it's school. People go to school because of society's expectation to succeed academically. Instead of training to be successful, we should focus more on what we need to do to be happy. If people would spend their time developing a skill from when they were young we would have more great artists and musicians in the world. Parents teach us not to think for ourselves. They figure we are too young or naïve or immature to make our own decisions. This can be true but we need to be allowed to make our own mistakes and then have to face the consequences so that we will be able to think independently and make good decisions.

For every action there is a reaction. Whether we know it or not, being raised by our parents helps us as much as it harms us. It is a challenge to observe their weaknesses and absorb their strengths. To do so you must try to understand them: where they came from, why they do what they do, and think what they think. To do this we must challenge authority. For most, this is opposite of their parents' wishes but is natural to want to do.

Challenging authority is necessary for social growth. If we just went around being sheep all of our lives things would never change the way we want them to. Revolution used to be called heresy, which was punishable by death. Those in control want to stay in control so they will try to suppress freethinking. Change is the only constant. If we are to be prepared for change we cannot be attached.

Being socially inclined can get you anything and everything in life. Oprah is the richest woman in America and all she does is talk to people. It's not who you are, it's who you know. That saying is very true and the way to know the right people and then to be successful is to be charismatic. Your parents tell you not to talk to strangers. Maybe we should just be taught how to read people a little better before we make any judgments. Teaching our kids to be antisocial doesn't seem to be good for their future success.

My parents have been clean and sober for over twenty years. I have been to A.A. meetings all my life, so I have been taught that drugs and alcohol are bad, destructive things, which is too vague. If I had been told about drugs rather than what can happen when you use them to excess, I would have been less likely to use them. When you're high, everything seems perfect. No worries or inhibitions. Things aren't as perfect as they seem. Drugs greatly diminish your desire to succeed in life and to work hard.

The reason I believe drugs such as marijuana and LSD are illegal is because they cause people to ask questions that would not be asked otherwise. People will question the rules, standards, and morals of the dysfunctional society we live in. This is the basis of change, revolution, and upheaval. The government controls and standardizes media and goods and everything else so that people will trust that the government knows what's in our best interest. They want and need to control thought in order to still be considered a fundamental "democratic" society. People who do not believe that authority should be accountable to the people it governs are probably not happy with their lives.

I believe that a strong relationship is built on trust. My mother always told me that relationships are built on integrity. This isn't true. If telling the truth will disrupt the relationship more than lying, then you should lie. I would rather be able to honestly tell my parents what I do when I'm outside of the house than be scared of being punished for what they think is wrong. Punishment shouldn't be based on opinion of what is right and what is wrong. People should be punished on the intention of their actions, not the actions themselves.

I think cooperation is a crucial part to a functional family unit. Everyone wants certain things, and about ninety percent of the time those things will be different, which is why you have to cooperate with each other to satisfy everyone. If one person is not getting what they want and they don't at least tell the other person about it, then their dissatisfaction will come through in other ways. One person will be thinking the situation has mutual satisfaction when it doesn't, or one person will be rude and the other won't know why, so they will be rude back and it will become an endless cycle of putdowns and comebacks.

If you are not a respectable person with respect for yourself, then why would others respect you? Sometimes parents have to cater to their kids because if you don't spoil them a little bit then they might feel unloved. You have to take time out to show that you care about their wants, not just their needs. Sometimes this means not doing what you want to, but as long as your children are respectful to you then you should be respectful to them. Respect is earned, so give your kids a reason to respect you and others.

I would say my parents are great parents. They have done their job as best as they know how. I wish everyone would be taught from a young age, as I was, that anything is possible.

*Sixteen-year-old **J.R.** likes people who think for themselves. What J.R. likes about himself is his charisma, sense of humor, and dreadlocks. He is inspired by his friends and "revolutionary music." His hobbies are snowboarding, networking, loving and making music. What is his goal? "Total freedom."*

I HAVE A WAY OF BEING
ALL MY SISTERS. PEOPLE
CONSIDER ME THE
QUIET ONE OF THE GROUP
BUT I AM LOUD IN MY
MIND.

-La'Quinta Williams

A Heart We Can Share

La'Quinta Williams

My mom has always been a hard-working woman. When she was twenty-six years old she lived in Kansas City, Kansas, in a house with her husband Elvin, three children, and another on the way. When her husband died, my mother was left a single parent of three, soon to be four. Her three children were my sisters Sherita, Janel, and Latasha. She was pregnant with my brother Elvin.

Later, after my mom met my dad, he moved in to help her with the children. My mom had another two girls, my sister Liera and me. When we were three and five years old, my mom and dad got married. Five years later, we moved to Seattle, Washington, and my brother Michael was born. Times were hard, but we made ends meet. When my mom got pregnant with my little sister Mercedez is when she decided that was enough children: six girls and two boys!

People think it's interesting that we are a family of so many girls. Sherita is the oldest. She is twenty-three. She has two baby boys named Keivonte, four years old, and Jha'Quez, three years old. In nine months, Sherita is going to have another baby. But she won't be able to keep it, so she will have to give it to my other sister Latasha. Not having custody of any of her kids is really hard for her, but it isn't always easy for her to be a good mother. Sometimes she has trouble controlling her temper and just goes wild. I think what she really needs is love and comfort. I try to be near her as much as possible because I know she's been through a lot with losing her children and her father, and it feels good for her to have her sisters around.

Janel is the second oldest. She is twenty-two years old. She also has children. Her son, Leland Jr., is four years old and her daughter, Jae'Shanel, is two years old. Janel has been in and out of bad relationships, but she always manages to get through. She happily lives on her own now and is really taking care of herself. Janel is the sister I go to when I need to get away from home because she always gives me a break. Of all of us girls, Janel is the most like my mom. She is very passionate and loving and she cares about a lot of people.

Latasha, twenty, is the third oldest. She doesn't have any kids yet but she works at a daycare so I'm sure that she loves kids. She goes through relationship problems every now and then but she always manages to handle them the right way. Latasha is very loud and outgoing. She has her times when she will be somewhat quiet, but those times don't last very long. Of all the girls, you could say Latasha is the one who is most different. She does her own thing and she always seems to get into fights with girls. I guess she doesn't like to be around girls. But overall, she is very sweet and caring about her family and loved ones.

Liera is the fourth oldest girl. She is seventeen years old. Liera is like my best friend because we do so much together. She helps me with problems and I help her with problems. Sometimes we have disagreements, but we never argue. She is very kind and sensitive.

She is not ashamed of the things she does. I would say she is more like my dad than my mom because she keeps a sound mind and talks freely.

My youngest sister is Mercedez. She is five years old. She has a really big heart for someone so young. If one of us is feeling bad, she always kisses us on our cheeks and it always makes it better. She loves to draw pictures for us and then we hang them on our walls to show appreciation. Mercedez is really sensitive and she cares about her family a lot. She reminds people of me when I was her age. I think she will be like me when she gets older.

Then comes me. My name is La'Quinta. I am fifteen years old. I am really sensitive but I do stand up for myself. I like to share my feelings and listen to other people's feelings. In a way, I am like each and every one of my sisters. I think I have a piece of each of their personalities. Like Sherita, I am strong in my heart. Like Janel, I go through relationship problems and always manage them the right way. Like Latasha, I have a sense of humor and always find time to laugh. Like Liera, I always focus on the things going on around me and try to solve them. And like Mercedez, I have a big heart and I love to comfort people when they cry. I have a way of being all my sisters. People consider me the quiet one of the group but I am loud in my mind.

All of us together, we get along great. My mom likes having so many girls because we always have someone to run to. It might seem like a small thing, but we can all do hair really well, which is important when you have so many girls in a family, especially on special occasions. Also, having so many sisters makes my brothers feel confident because we are always there for support.
I would say that we are a pretty happy family, and even though we all don't live together we still share a really big heart.

"I like the fact that I care about people's feelings, and I like to express my feelings." This is what fifteen-year-old **La'Quinta Williams** *likes most about herself. Her hobbies include talking on the phone, singing, dancing, shopping, and watching movies. Her family and people from church inspire her. She hopes that her essay inspires you.*

...HAPPILY EVER AFTER

FAMILY CAN BE THAT

IRRITATION OF THE

NAGGING SIBLINGS, OR

THE WARMTH OF YOUR

MOTHER'S ARMS

AROUND YOU IN A TIME OF

NEED.

-AMANDA HENRITZE

My Guardian Angel

Amanda Henritze

What is family? To me family is not only the blood that runs through your veins but the feeling of someone being there always. Family can be that irritation of the nagging siblings, or the warmth of your mother's arms around you in a time of need. Family could also be the friend who has dried your tears and stood by you through thick and thin. I consider friends a part of my family, particularly one friend, Hannah Evans.

I was born in Wyoming, but then moved to Seattle. I remember this girl across the alleyway welcoming me to come and play with her when I first moved to Seattle. Little did I know this friendly girl Hannah would become a part of who I became, my life and my family. Playing with her every chance I had, I started to grow close to her. Hannah and I were best friends. I remember the first time I went to her house. We watched Ace Ventura Pet Detective, and cracked up the whole time, having the time of our lives. Growing up I didn't always have Hannah as my ray of sunshine. When living with my father we moved a lot for financial reasons, so I had to say good-bye to my best friend, help pack up the house, and leave my neighborhood. Being only five years old I couldn't really write her letters or even really call her. So it was just a flat-out good-bye. Back then I didn't know that Hannah was going to be my Guardian Angel.

As time passed I started elementary school and made other friends. In about the second grade I started taking the yellow school bus. The first day I went with my grandmother. We walked up to the bus stop and I saw a long line of kids. I stared, intimidated, and snuck behind my grandma. I looked and I scoped out all the kids. Hannah and I made eye contact and she screamed, "AMANDA, IS THAT YOU?" We ran toward each other and held one another in our arms. I couldn't believe it. My best friend was back. From then on we were together.

Sometimes we would go to the Ballard Boys and Girls Club. We would chase the boys around and dance and sing to the Spice Girls. I remember once when Hannah and I were sitting underneath the pool table with my boyfriend and her ex-boyfriend, Jonathan. She made me kiss Jonathan. First it started with the hand, then cheek, and finally the lips. After that, time started passing surprisingly fast.

In the fifth grade I spent the night over at Hannah's house. We decided to sneak out to go roller-skating (at the time the rink was the "place to be"). I met all her friends from school and started to learn slang, such as "you smell like Peaches." We were pretty slick for fifth graders, except I told my mom what had happened because another mom was going to if I didn't.

That summer my mom, my sisters, and I moved four blocks away from where Hannah lived. Going to the same middle school led us to become sisters. Spending every day together, she would watch over me and help me whenever I needed a shoulder. All I would have to do is run a couple blocks and my security blanket was put on me with warmth.

After going through all the middle-school drama we were on

our way to high school, every girl's "dream," and I had my angel to help guide me. I felt like the luckiest person ever. Even though we had no classes together we would still hang out constantly. Somehow we both weren't doing so hot in school, so during tenth grade Hannah switched to a different school. Still stuck to the drama, I stayed behind to try again. Well, for me, Ballard wasn't really a learning type of school. After listening to Hannah talk about how she was finally doing well in her new school and loving it, I decided to look at my options.

After a couple months I made a decision to either go to Learning Center North, the school Hannah attends, or Indian Heritage. At that point in my life I had to learn that I couldn't always have someone hold my hand, so I decided to go get my high school diploma instead of a GED. It is really hard for me not to have an angel over my shoulder to help me make the right choices, but I am growing up and I had to face it sometime.

Hannah has helped me through more struggles than I could ever remember, from my dad, to boys, to drugs. She has always been there for me, no matter what has happened. She picks me up when I can no longer stand and she helps show me the right path, following it is my decision. Now living in Shoreline, I don't see my Guardian Angel every day anymore, but I feel her presence wherever I go. We spend hours talking on the phone about what's been going on, and every time she answers her phone I thank God I have a person in my life to help guide me to the right path. It's different now, though. Instead of holding my hand and watching over me, she now guides me with her words.

No longer having that hand to hold, I started down the wrong path, losing touch with my real self and getting into stuff that no one would ever want to be involved in. Hannah did struggle to help me, but I was angry that she could no longer assist me the way she used to. But still I would go back to her, or she would come back to me, picking me up one last time, dusting me off and sending me on my way.

Sitting here reminiscing about all that has happened I wish I could go back to the way things were, but I love our relationship now. Hannah has made me grow in more than one way. I don't think I show my gratitude to her because I am still a little angry

57

that our relationship is not like it used to be. One of the many things my angel has taught me is that things change, life changes, and you have to accept that. You can't grow without pain and change.

So thank you, Hannah, for helping me grow and learn. We will always be there for each other, and I thank God every day to be blessed with a friend like you and I pray to never lose you. You have been there from my first bee sting to my first drunk night (Valentine's Day). You are my best friend and the only one who knows me better than I know myself. Thank you for never turning your back on me.

"I think it's cool," sixteen-year-old
Amanda Henritze *says of the
826 Seattle project. "I've never
done anything like this." She enjoys
making people laugh, drawing, and
eating. She is motivated by "anyone
who has been through pain and
conquered a problem."*

I MEAN, COME ON, IF YOU ONLY SAID NICE THINGS, YOU WOULDN'T TALK VERY MUCH, WOULD YOU?

-DAVID BULLOCK

[Insert Title Here]

David Bullock

I bet the only reason you are reading this is because the title is so weird. Heh. Well… family… family… I don't particularly like my family.

I've always been told if you can't say anything nice, don't say anything at all, but screw that, there's no point to that, besides, that's not any fun at all. I mean, come on, if you only said nice things, you wouldn't talk very much, would you? If people just said nice things, the world would be very boring. Although we wouldn't have as much drama, which is a definite plus, we wouldn't have very much to say.

My mom's fine, I like my mom. I mean, life with my mom isn't the same as with my dad, I'm not grounded all the time, and I actually even get stuff for doing good things. Well, I guess you might want to know more about her. Her favorite show is America's Funniest Videos. She doesn't really like the people being stupid; she really likes the babies and animals. She's forty-seven and works at a grocery store. We live with my grandma in Seattle, and take care of her because she is eighty-nine and has had knee surgery recently. My mom goes out with her friends on the weekends and listens to music. Mostly she goes to Pioneer Square, places like the New Orleans and other blues clubs. As you probably guessed, she likes blues. She also likes some jazz, rock... and, well, some of just about every kind of music there is. Her favorite color is purple. Also, she likes to tell and hear stupid jokes. For example, "What did the sea monster have for lunch?" "Fish and Ships!" or, "Where does Dracula go waterskiing?" "Lake Eerie!" Mostly she tells these jokes to little kids, like pre-preschool and early elementary kids. She loves kids that age.

I'm glad I have my mom. Otherwise I would have to live with my dad, like I did for almost a year. It was horrible. I was always in trouble. I didn't get anything nice, but my dad and my stepmom did. Like, my bed was their old bed set thing, and theirs was a new frame. I'm not sure about the mattress, I think it was new too, but I don't know. Also, I got my clothes from Kmart and Target, and they got theirs from nice places such as Nordstrom.

My dad, well, he's okay, but he's always been so whipped. He never calls the shots. I had to live with him and my second step-mom for almost a year, and you could tell she was making up the rules as she went along and he was just the messenger. I got grounded for every insignificant thing. If I didn't do something to their satisfaction, I got grounded. I got grounded if I didn't get As and Bs. A C is still passing, so is a D, so why did I get grounded for those?

I ran away from my dad's house, all the way to Seattle from Puyallup, because my second stepmom grabbed me and cut my arm with her nails. I don't know why she did it, we were supposed to go somewhere, but she got all pissy with me so I left. I was eating a bowl of cereal and she got all pissed at me when I was ready to go. I guess she thought I wasn't ready or something. Whatever. Like I said, she grabbed me and so I left.

My first stepmom was worse, though. I had to write a thank-you letter to my grandma when I was seven, and I couldn't get my handwriting to her satisfaction, so she said I couldn't watch TV. I said fine, and went in the living room and just sat there. She came out and grabbed me by the hair and pulled me every which way, and I didn't even have much hair! I mean, it was summer, and I had gotten a crew cut like two or three months before. Thankfully, they are no longer together.

Now, my uncle, man, he is a jerk. He's trying to get me and my mom kicked out of my grandma's, when my mom and I take care of her, and I know he's not going to. He's bitching about how she, my grandma, doesn't have any freedom, when she has a lot of freedom, my mom and I aren't there most of the day. I'm at school, and she is working. We try to help her as much as possible, but sometimes she gets all grouchy at us for it.

Well, that's about it. That's all the family I really know and/or talk to. The only person I really have nice things to say about is my mom, maybe it is due to the fact that she raised me since she and my dad split up when I was, like, one, or maybe it's because she is actually a good person. It could even be both, but I will leave that up to your speculation.

*Fifteen-year-old **David Bullock** hopes to become a professional musician. He can be found playing the guitar, and Kurt Cobain inspires him. David would describe himself as "strange, goofy."*

I STOOD AND WATCHED MY DAD DRIVE AWAY FROM THE TRAIN STATION. MY MIND WAS A MESS. I WAS A MESS. I FELT LIKE CRYING. I REMEMBER HEARING ALL OF THE USUAL CITY NOISES: THE CARS SPEEDING BY AND BITS AND PIECES OF PEOPLE'S CONVERSATIONS AS THEY PASSED.

-ROLAND KURSAR

A "Slight" Inconvenience

Roland Kursar

I stood and watched my dad drive away from the train station. My mind was a mess. I was a mess. I felt like crying. I remember hearing all of the usual city noises: the cars speeding by and bits and pieces of people's conversations as they passed. I thought to myself, what's going to happen? Is Seattle going to be my new home?

I lived in St. Helens, Oregon. St. Helens was a town where if you sneezed, everyone knew within five minutes. I was a teenager who thought that I shouldn't have to follow any of my parents' rules. I attended an alternative school and was at the top of my class. But in early December 2005 I began to get into trouble at school.

The trouble I was getting into was just normal teenage misbehavior. It was nothing serious until the day another student and I got into a verbal fight during a field trip to the Ape Caves in Washington. We exchanged inappropriate words and left it at that. When we returned from the field trip I was approached by a teacher and informed that a few other students and I would not be allowed to return to school until a meeting could take place with our parents and the school staff. I can't go to into details about the whole incident due to pending legal actions.

My meeting took place the following week. As I walked into the room I saw all of the teachers from my school sitting at a large table in the middle of the room. I was surprised because I thought there would be only two or three teachers. My parents and I took seats at the table. I wasn't prepared for what they were about to tell me. The head teacher said that because of my actions they were going to hold an expulsion hearing to determine whether or not I would be allowed to return to school. When I heard the word "expulsion" my life felt as if it were over. I could feel my eyes tearing up, but I wasn't going to allow myself to cry. I clenched my fists below the table and finished listening to the staff talk. Little did I know my life was about to take a huge turn.

On December 14, 2005, my expulsion hearing took place in the district office next door to the school. My dad and I sat in the lobby as we waited for the hearing to take place. The expulsion officer came and told us that he was ready and led us to the hearing room. At this time I heard evidence against me and had a chance to defend myself. Forty-five minutes later, at the end of the hearing, the expulsion officer told us that he would make his determination within a few weeks.

I had already planned to spend time over Christmas break with my sister Sari and her husband, Alex, in Seattle. By now I desperately needed a vacation. My sister and brother-in-law and I had all talked about the possibility of me moving in with them. I thought that this was an excellent idea, because it would open up so many more opportunities for me. There is one word that comes to mind when I think of them: SUCCESS.

After my dad left me at the train station I went in and picked up my ticket, then grabbed a bite to eat while waiting to board the train. I couldn't stop thinking about what had been going on over the past few weeks. It was a depressing feeling that lingered like a storm cloud in my head for months. The train ride to Seattle seemed never-ending. I was so excited to get to visit Sari and Alex that every stop the train made felt as if it lasted for an hour. When I got to their house, Sari said, "You have more bags than usual." By this time I had already made the decision that I was going to move in with them but hadn't told anyone.

Each day, they would ask me if I had made my decision, and even though my mind was made up, I didn't know how to tell them. I was uncomfortable accepting such a generous offer. They kept asking, though, and telling me they weren't trying to force me into anything. "It's your choice," Sari said. After three days, we finally all sat down together and talked about it. Even though my old school ended up not expelling me, there was no way in hell I was going back. I said yes to Sari and Alex, I would love to move in with them.

Having my sister and brother-in-law open up their house to me was like winning the lottery. They have been married for almost four years. About a year before I moved in with them, they graduated from Western Washington University in Bellingham. Sari earned her degree in sociology and Alex earned his in computer science. Shortly after they graduated they moved to Seattle. Since then they have both found good jobs. For them to take responsibility of a teenager is so greatly appreciated. I wouldn't be where I am without their help, and my parents'.

When I lived in Oregon my after-school life consisted of hanging out with friends and doing nothing productive. Since I moved to Seattle my whole attitude toward life has changed. I have realized that life is not just about play. You have responsibilities and have to do things that you don't want to do to go somewhere in life. I have gotten a good job and am currently working on graduating this year. Since my move to Seattle I think that I have bettered my relationships with all of my family members. I have learned that having a family that cares can make all the difference in the world.

What are seventeen-year-old **Roland Kursar's** *goals? "Too many to list." He can say what he likes most about himself, though: "My character and who I am." His hobbies are using My Space, playing video games, and going new places, and he is inspired by friends and family.*

"We'll be GLAD TO SEE YOU this FALL," they finally said. THOSE were THE WORDS I HAD longed for, WORDS of ACCEPTANCE.

-Erica Nicole Lee

MY TRUTH

Erica Nicole Lee

I have a good home and always have. I had shoes, clothes, a full belly, and a roof over my head, but somehow I still felt empty. My family loved me and I loved them with all my heart, but something was missing. Something deep inside of me was longing for a feeling of acceptance in society. I wasn't one of the skinny blonde girls that I grew up around. I was—I am—me. Brown. For this I was taunted, teased, and abused. I was scared, shy, and neglected. I longed for people I could admire and fit in with.

Middle school was by far the hardest time in my life. I hated it. I would have never done such cruel things to someone as were done to me. I am still scared from all of the hardships I overcame. It feels like there's a hole in my heart where my early adolescent memories should be.

I had a best friend, Kat. We got into so much trouble that our parents didn't want us hanging out together. She went on a three-week school field trip to China after having knee surgery. On a hike there she fell, almost to her death, but somehow she cheated death. It was after her, but she was destined to come back home to her family and friends. When she did, we all got to hang out and play softball. It was the beginning of the season and the first time she was able to play since her knee surgery.

It was a great game, although we goofed off half the time and lost the game. We still had fun. After all, that's all we cared about—having fun. We all went our separate ways after the game, but we were going to meet at a friend's house later that night. Hours went by before we realized that Kat and the people she was with still hadn't shown up.

I was starting to get worried, so I called a friend. She said that Kat got hit by a train and was hurt bad. I was thinking she had a broken back or neck or something, but then we got the phone call. She didn't make it. I freaked out and burst into tears. My life was instantly changed, dramatically, forever. I felt as if I was living life blind, deaf, and totally oblivious to the world around me. I didn't care about anything anymore. I didn't care who I hurt, worried, or betrayed. All I wanted was my best friend back.

Going through that at such an unstable time in my life made it even more challenging for me to get ahead. I was depressed and didn't believe in myself. I slept all day, and when I was awake, I cried. I became increasingly rebellious, angry, cruel, and downright nasty to the ones I loved. I felt that I couldn't love or care about anyone or anything in fear of losing it. I couldn't feel that pain again.

I became engulfed in rage and fury. I sank into a deep dark shell of depression, not even wanting to go on. Even the most beautiful days felt like they had no meaning. I was nasty and rude to my family, the ones who took care of me all of my life, and it wasn't their fault. I regret everything I have ever done to hurt my family.

School was the last thing on my mind, and when I was there, I was there to party. I was on a rapid downward spiral to a life of hurt and resentments. In my second year at a high school full of mostly wealthy Caucasian students, I felt as if my morals had been burnt up in an eruption of negative emotions.

I slept through most of my high school days until I had a meeting with the woman I dreaded most—the principal. She told me that I didn't belong there, that it was wrong for me. I felt like saying, "DUH!!!" I didn't, but I wish I had expressed myself. I thought it was a whole crock of mess, but my mom (thank God for her) told me to hear her out. The principal recommended some schools that I had heard of and one I hadn't: American Indian Heritage.

I was actually interested in this one. It sounded unique, like me. In early September 2003, I went to an interview at American Indian Heritage Middle College High School—WHEW, that's long. I wasn't nervous. I was interested and intrigued. When I walked into the school I felt a sense of home. It was comfortable, relaxing, and new.

They asked questions like "Why do you want to be here?" and "What are your interests?" Right away I was overwhelmed with excitement, hoping to get accepted. I don't know what came over me, but I felt this was where I wanted to be. They talked with me and then my mom, then us together. "We'll be glad to see you this fall," they finally said. Those were the words I had longed for, words of acceptance. Now that I had the chance to make a clean start, I was going to make the most of it. Not many people get a second chance. I am so blessed.

September 29, 2003, was my first day at AIH and the first day of the rest of my life. I didn't feel out of place or nervous. For once I wasn't one of the few; I was one of the majority. It felt so good; right away I felt comfortable and welcome. I felt understood and interested. I had found myself, my culture, and my people.

The biggest problem I'd always had with going to school was getting out of bed in the morning to make it on time. I improved at first... slightly. Hey, at least I was going and wanted to go! I am definitely not a morning person, but now I had a feeling of guilt from not being there. As time went on and I became more in tune with the focus of the school, I couldn't wait to go to school the next day. I grew closer to the school and the people in it and gained the motivation and dedication to go every day.

My name is Erica Lee and I am from the Cherokee Nation. I would have never introduced myself using those words had I not been blessed with the experience at AIH. I had never been taught the hardships my people went through, including assimilation. The focus of the school is to teach from the west looking east, to look at history from the Native perspective, to teach and express all of the anguish and pain the Natives went through: boarding schools, government supplied commodities, reservations, and lies. I bet you never knew. A whole culture, a way of life, was abolished and decimated by the Anglo-Saxons.

At AIH, they tell the truth. They keep the spirit alive. No matter what happens, so long as the drum beats, Indian people will live on. I've learned many Native teachings there. I've learned that we must respect everything around us, even things that are not human or alive. I've learned to respect and love myself for who I am, and not let anyone bring me down, no matter what. This is the thing I will always hold near and dear to my heart. Black, white, yellow, red, green or magenta, we are all here together and we need to care about ourselves and each other to make the world turn in balance. I am so thankful for my school. They truly are my second family. Thank you to my teachers and fellow classmates who helped me learn and understand how to be me, and to love, honor, and cherish myself. Without them I wouldn't have known about my ancestors and my history. My truth is that I have been taught the Native way and it saved my life. Now I know and now I can teach. The teachers at AIH really helped me come a long way, and I owe my life to them. Without their guidance and respect, I wouldn't be graduating this spring,

I found where I belong. I found my family.

Successful minorities inspire eighteen-year-old **Erica Nicole Lee.** *She herself is strong, passionate, curious and motivated. You can find her wrangling dogs, reading, writing, beading, and painting. She plans on one day being successful in an animal-related field.*

I GOT OFF THE PHONE,
THINKING, DANG, I LOVE
FIGHTING, BUT I'D RATHER
SEE A FIGHT THEN BE IN
ONE. I WAS THINKING,
WHAT IF SHE BEATS ME UP?
WHAT IF I BEAT HER UP?
EITHER WAY SOMEONE IS
GOING TO GET BEAT. OH
WELL.

-GINA ALLISCE MICKLE

THE FIGHT

Gina Allisce Mickle

Yesterday one of my friends called me about fifteen minutes after I got home. She's like a big sister to me but from a different hood (the Central District on the other side of Seattle—the CD). Her name is Dana. I met Dana my freshmen year in school, 2005. I started to kick it with her, and the relationship between us became strong, and then I became part of her kinfolk.

Well, out of nowhere she says, "Gina, you wanna beat this girl up?"

Lots of times close friends will get someone to fight their battles if the other person's too young or too old for that person to fight.

I'm like, "Why?"

She said, "Hold on, talk to Montez."

So Montez gets on the phone saying, "Who's this? Who's this?"

I was like, "Montez, it's Gina from Marshall, the one from the
South End. But anyways, what happen?"

He was like, "Man, this beezy almost got me shot and I could
of died. She ratted us out to the South End n----s earlier."

I was like, "Oh, that's the reason why you want me to fight the
girl!"

"Yeah, man, the girl goes to Nova, and if you beat her up then
we'll pay you, but I mean if you don't, then whoever beats her up
will get paid."

"Oh, let me talk to Dana."

"Gina! Are you going to fight her?"

I hesitated.

"Man, yeah, I guess."

I got off the phone, thinking, dang, I love fighting, but I'd rather see a fight then be in one. I was thinking, what if she beats me
up? What if I beat her up? Either way someone is going to get beat.
Oh well. By this time my friend Tashi had called me from Cali.

She was like, "You might as well just shoot her and get it over."

I laughed hella hard. "Tashi! This is not Cali, where we shoot
people, and plus I'd rather just torture the female instead. It's easier
for me."

The next day after school, Dana brought some of my homies to
the school. All the CD n----s were getting me so hyphy. I was so
ready, I wanted to kill her.

Dana came up to me saying, "Are you ready for her?"

"Yeah, I'm ready."

When we got off the bus, me, Dana, and all my homies walked
to Garfield. We were on top of the "Pyramid," the kick'n-it spot
next to Ezell's Chicken where the fight was going to be. Twenty to
twenty-five people were around. They were so hyped. So I walks up
to the girl I'm going to fight, and I looked her up and down, and
I threw the first punch by stealing on her. She fell on the ground,
and I hit her at a fast, constant pace. When she tried to get up, I
jumped on her back, hitting her on the side of her head. I jumped
off her back, and, round two, I started fighting her again. She
seemed so mad, getting beat up by someone that was shorter than
her. She was calling me all types of names. I really wasn't bothered
by what she was saying.

Dana grabbed me, thinking the fight was over. She was like, "Girl, you smashed her, you smashed her. She didn't want none." Then out of nowhere the girl grabs my shirt from behind and my shirt rips.

I was like, "It's over. You don't want me to beat you up again, do you?"

She just walked away looking hella stupid.

Montez came up to me and gave me forty bucks, and he shook my hand and was like, "Thanks, cuz—you know, you should be from the CD because we know you would be down for us."

"Oh, thanks anyway, but you didn't have to pay me."

"Gimme the money if you don't want it!"

"No, I'll keep it."

Man, the fight between me and that girl was the talk of '06. The friendship between me and Dana has lasted all through everything. Having a friend be a big sister like Dana means you stick together no matter what the factors are: fighting, bailing one another out, money, you name it. That's how good the bond and connection we will always have is.

*In a few years, you might find sixteen-year-old **Gina Allisce Mickle** at Cascadia Community College studying to become an engineer. These days you will find her dancing at house parties and hanging out with friends. Gina describes herself as an energetic and hilarious person who is inspired by positive people.*

I'VE HAD MY **HEART BROKEN**

FROM BOYS 'N SUCH **BEFORE**

BUT THIS **KIND** OF **HEARTBREAK**

AFFECTS **SO MUCH** MORE

SEE, UNLIKE BOYS, **A FAMILY**

IS SUPPOSED TO **TOUGH** IT **OUT**

TO BE THERE WHEN **LOVE IS NEEDED**

ISN'T THAT WHAT **FAMILY'S ABOUT?**

-KATHERINE GRAVES

HUSH, LITTLE MAMA, DONT YOU CRY

Katherine Graves

The following poems depict members of my family, which include my daughter, my mother, my sister, my brother, and my father.

HUSH, LITTLE MAMA

Hush, little mama, don't you cry
The tears aren't meant for show
The hurt and pain and love you've lost
Isn't for the world to know
Hush, little mama, it'll be okay
Just think of your little girl

And how you'd never leave her side
Like your mother did your own
Hush, little mama, you'll see her again
After all, look how far you've come
She'll always be your little sister
Your mom can't take away that love
Hush, little mama, he's sorry now
Just look into his eyes
He is your brother after all
It's better to forgive, than live without him in your life
Hush, little mama, don't worry now
Your home will be stable one day
Your dad is getting better now
Everything will be okay
So hush, little mama, don't you cry
Forgive, forget, and predict
For the love you lost, the love you gained
And for the love you still miss

BRIANNA: EXPECTING

Your time is coming soon
In no time you'll be here
The end of these nine months
Is becoming oh so near
I'm nervous and excited
At the same time, I'm afraid
But the fact is I'm a mother
So for you, I'll be brave
Now the biggest responsibility of my life
Is to care for another
No longer looked at as a teen
But now a teen mother
Most look down on a child born
To a mother of my youth
But a baby is a blessing
I will not refuse

Even though it's early
You entered my life at the perfect time
And because of you I value
What'll happen in my life

To My Mother:
I Am Sorry I Can't Be Perfect

I screamed as loud as I could
But my cries were never heard
I poured my heart out to you
Yet you never heard a word
I don't know what I am doing
Or if what I plan to do is right
I need someone to talk to
My chest feels so tight
I've had my heart broken
From boys 'n such before
But this kind of heartbreak
Affects so much more
See, unlike boys, a family
Is supposed to tough it out
To be there when love is needed
Isn't that what family's about?
I wish I knew who you are
So I could let go of who you were
What happened to my mother?
Could you tell her I miss her?
You added salt to a wound
That's sensitive to a breeze
Not to mention opened a scar
And again caused it to bleed
You make me feel the same way
You did years ago
Maybe things weren't meant to change
Because again I feel alone
So tell me was it worth it

My heart broken
So you could smile at him
Is his love better
Than your daughter's?
I'm sorry for trying again
Are you happy now?
Can I make you proud?
Will anything that I ever do be good enough for you?

GABBY

Please don't forget me
I love you, I swear
Please know that it's not my fault
That I can't be there
I want to say I love you
If I could only have those words
I'd scream how much I love you
If I knew that I'd be heard
If I could only hold you
Even if it'd be the last time
For you to know I love you
And that you're always on my mind
How can she do this?
She has no heart
She seems perfectly content
With keeping us apart
Do you remember when you last saw me?
When we said goodbye...
Even though you were too young
To understand why I cried
I remember it clearly
Just like it were today
If only I knew it'd be the last time
So much more I would say
And no matter what, my love for you
With time will never change

Sisters have a bond, built strong to remain
Do you think about me?
Did you know we're in the same town?
Would you recognize my face,
If I stood amongst a crowd?
I will see you again
How ever long it may be
But while I am waiting
Gabby, please, don't forget me

Hermano

I really just started thinking
How dead to me you are
Then I thought of all the times we shared
And it breaks my heart
I wish that I could yell at you
How could you do this to me?
I wish that I could go back
Back to when we were family
After everything we went through
You know you were my rock
How dare you try and lie to me!
Have you forgot?!
The way that I was there for you
And believed you when no one else would
And all those times you gave me faith
When no one else could
You are my brother, my blood!
The only person that has lasted
You were the only constant in my life this far
So tell me, was it worth it?
All the things I told you
And everything you shared with me
It was all bullshit, wasn't it?
Goodbye, family!

FORGIVING MY FATHER

Can you cry
Do you know what pain feels like on the inside
Can you deal
With knowing everyone who is supposed to love you
    could care less
Could you lie
Can you keep a smile on your face while you're
    dying inside
Could you look at yourself in the mirror, and honestly
    know who it is you see
Could you break from the chains that hold you and
    learn to breathe?
I don't cry
Because I know what pain feels like on the inside
Forced to deal
With knowing everyone who is supposed to love me
    could care less
Still, I lie
I keep a smile on my face while I'm dying inside
When I look at myself in the mirror, I honestly don't know
    who it is I see
Bound by these chains that hold me and I can't breathe
Can you feel
Do you know what causes pain when it is real
Can you cope
With knowing things will never be the same again
Do you know
How to love someone after they've left you alone
Could you search your soul and honestly be satisfied with
    what you seek
Could you break from the chains that hold you and
    learn to breathe?
I don't feel
Because I know what causes pain when it is real
Forced to cope
With knowing things will never be the same again

Still I know
How to love someone after they've left me alone
If I searched my soul I honestly don't know what it'd be that
   I would seek
Bound by these chains that hold me and I can't breathe

*"I am realistic and dedicated. When I have a goal I strive for it." That is what seventeen-year-old **Katherine Graves** likes most about herself. One of the goals she is striving toward is to publish her own book. In addition to writing, she enjoys singing and reading. Her greatest inspiration is her one-and-half-year-old daughter, Brianna.*

INSIDE HE KNEW HE
WOULD FIND ONLY DEATH,
BUT HE NEEDED TO KNOW
NONETHELESS. HE PUSHED
ON THE WOODEN DOOR, HIS
RIGHT HAND FALLING TO
THE SWORD HIS FATHER
HAD GIVEN HIM BEFORE HE
HAD SET OUT MORE THAN A
WEEK AGO.

-JOSEPH D. BRYANT

THE START OF A NEW
AN EXCERPT FROM A NOVEL IN PROGRESS

Joseph D. Bryant

The snow had stopped falling hours before, but the wind was as harsh as ever. Violent gusts blew about the frozen land, creating small whirlwinds of snow and ice. The sun, usually shining her smile down upon the land, cowered behind ominous clouds. Navanod looked up to the sky, cursing as he trekked further through the forest. Deprived of food and sleep, he hated everything this minute, believing himself not far from death. The only thing that kept him moving was the thought of seeing his family once again. He wanted to share his vision with his father, tell his mother of Frostedge's magnificent beauty, and give Alyna a gift. He reached into his tundra bison hide coat and produced an elongated piece of cloth no longer than his forefinger, and slowly unfolded it, revealing the brilliance of the object.

He ceased his stride and gazed into the silver-green crystal. After a pause, he picked up his walk.

The day after Navanod's sixteenth birthday, he embarked on a journey to an ice canyon known as Frostedge. He traveled for days with barely food or water, but somehow always managed to stay alive. When the boy had finally reached the ice canyon, he set out to search for the old man known as Nightseer: a blind prophet said to be as old as the land itself. When he finally found the elderly man, he began his Spirit Walk, a rite of passage among the barbarian peoples of Aarkana, the North Lands.

Nightseer gave the boy a medicine during the nights so that he would receive visions from the spirit realm, visions that would show him the path to being a man. When Navanod's visions finally did come, he saw a magnificent stag, like no other he had seen before. The beast was enveloped in a golden glow and his eyes were a piercing black. Then, as if the stag were merely an illusion, it faded away and the forest around it came alive, and ancient trees began to walk like a man. The venerable old man interpreted the vision as Navanod's Spirit Quest; he had to travel to the land of the living forests and take down the stag in his vision. The land of living forests was also known as the Mystical East, where the unexplained and magical thrived.

The boy slogged further up the hill, pushing himself to reach the rounded top. Upon reaching the peak of the hill, Navanod gazed across the land.

Luscious greenery stretched as far as the eye could see, and snow-capped mountains littered the scenery. It was a stunning view. Then, as if beauty became unreal, the sickest sight slaughtered the serene landscape. He could just barely make out the distinct shape of Stone City, the capital of Aarkana. He hadn't recognized it at first, but off in the distance, a cloud of menacing black rapidly polluted the air above the city. His heart sank and he screamed as he dashed down the hillside.

He kept running as fast as he possibly could in his state of lethargy until he reached the halfway point between the hill and the city. He could clearly make out the city walls and the fires that raged within, as well as the sight of corpses that littered the ground just outside the city walls. Navanod sprinted forward.

"Da, Ma!" he cried as he made his way to the massive stone wall. He walked slowly through the gates, pausing briefly to mourn the corpse of a childhood friend, then continued his journey inward. As he walked, the smoke choked him, but not quite enough to incapacitate him. The boy passed body upon body. He recognized many as his father's and mother's friends, but he did not stop to mourn them; his mind was focused elsewhere. He needed to know where his parents were.

Soon, Navanod found himself at the base of the door that led into his home. Inside he knew he would find only death, but he needed to know nonetheless. He pushed on the wooden door, his right hand falling to the sword his father had given him before he had set out more than a week ago. He entered the home.

The stench of burning flesh crashed into him, and he covered his nose with his sleeve as he moved inside. The sight he found was one he expected, but did not welcome. His mother's motionless body sat limply at the base of the stove in an abnormal position, a butcher's knife grasped in one hand. Blood trickled down her forehead from an unseen wound. He fell to his knees and wept silently. After a long moment of mourning, he rose back to his feet and immediately noticed the dead soldier lying in the next room. The dead man's hands clutched his throat and his eyes had rolled back into his skull. Navanod cracked a sick grin, knowing his mother had taken a few of the attackers out with her.

"Your father, have you discovered him?" A voice shattered the eerie silence of the massacre.

Navanod spun around, instinctively bringing his sword into a defensive position. "Who-" he stopped himself in mid-sentence when he recognized the tattered gray cloak that was wrapped around a man that stood in the doorway of the home. Gray, the Ranger.

"Gray..." he started, but the Ranger held up a hand and motioned him outside. Navanod obliged.

Once outside, Navanod fell against the house's wall and let out a deep sigh, fighting back tears. "What happened?"

Gray looked to the sky and folded his arms. After a long pause he began, "I've had a few minutes to search around the city. From the looks of everything, I'd say Darathan soldiers came from the southwest and entered the southern gates of the city, butchering all they could." The Ranger's voice held little sympathy as he went over the events that unfolded. As he spoke, Navanod's brow furrowed and his breathing quickened.

"How do you know all this, Ranger?" he barked.

Doolbwen "Gray" took a step back and glared at Navanod. "For just that reason, boy. I'm a Ranger; it is my duty to know how battles are won and lost. It's easy to tell how this battle was fought, if you just open your eyes and look around. Look around you!" the Ranger ordered, sweeping his arms. "Do you see all this? Look at the mass of bodies to the south of the city. Do you see how they are all men? Your father is down there." He witnessed the boy's eyes widen and he had to hold out an arm to keep Navanod from rushing away.

"Do you know what that information tells me? It tells me that Ryvax, your father, massed his warriors on the south of the city to stop the invaders from pushing inward. The Darathan soldiers are no fools, and I'm assuming that this was accomplished by one of the more superior units. They overwhelmed our warriors with sheer numbers and took the city in a little less than a few hours." Navanod's knees fell from under him and he collapsed to the snow-covered ground weeping. "Da," he whined, "ma—"

"—are dead. No use fretting about it. Now get up." Gray grabbed the boy by the arm and forced him up to his feet. "Your father was speared seven times before he fell. The body is pinned to the wall as a reminder to all those who travel here. You can see for yourself." The look on Gray's face horrified Navanod. There was not an ounce of emotion in his eyes, and not a quiver of sorrow in his voice.

Too shocked to respond appropriately, Navanod merely shook his head.

Gray let out a sigh and grabbed Navanod by the shoulders with both hands.

His grip was iron as he shook the boy forcefully. "Listen, boy, you have to learn to put these emotions behind you. Your father gave me the responsibility to show you the ways of the Ranger. Your training starts now. Sympathy and sorrow have no place within a Ranger. You must be numb! Do you understand? Your father is dead. Your mother is dead. Everyone in this city is—"

"Alyna!" Navanod had completely forgotten about the girl until this moment.

He pushed away from the Ranger and started down the street, but was swept off his feet by an unseen force and fell face-first to the snowy ground.

"Stupid child," Gray cursed as he pushed his foot onto the boy's back. "We don't have time to go searching for anyone. We've lingered too long as it is. So shut up, get up, and follow me. We're going to take some food and pack some essentials, then we'll be off." He released the pressure on Navanod's back and started away. Navanod rose to his feet, rubbing his sore back as he tried to keep himself from tears. "Where?" he croaked.

Gray stopped walking and looked at the sky. Navanod recognized his position as the Ranger's usual thinking stance. "To find your remaining family. Your brothers are to the south, and they are the last of your bloodline." The Ranger started again, and this time the boy followed.

* * *

The pair sat opposite each other around the small campfire. What was visible of the sun had set long ago, and now the only light in the skies came from the moon and the dancing stars. The clouds had separated a few hours before, and so the night was clear. The air, however, was as cold as ever and chilled both the Ranger's and the boy's bones.

A pot sat on the small fire, and inside was their dinner, although Navanod didn't know what they were eating that night. "What's in it?" he queried.

"Food." Gray responded, his voice carrying an irritated tone.

"What kind of food?" Navanod pressed.

"Good food." Again, the Ranger avoided the answer.

Annoyed by the obvious evasion, Navanod huffed and tightened the blanket on his shoulders, muttering under his breath.

"What was that?" Gray lifted his focus from the pot to look at the boy, a curious eyebrow cocked upward. "You didn't speak clearly."

Navanod's head shot up and looked at the Ranger, a look of disbelief crossed his face. "Wha—"

"The second thing you should know about us Rangers is that we have exceptional hearing. Call me an 'old man' again and you'll be eating worms until we reach your brothers."

The boy let his grip on his blanket loosen and he stared dumbfounded at the Ranger, his jaw hanging low.

After a few moments of silence the Ranger spoke. His voice was calm and even-toned.

"I've been trailing you since you started on your journey to Frostedge. Your father insisted that you could do it on your own. I convinced him otherwise. And a good thing I followed, too. There were quite a few times you would have starved to death, had I not helped.

"I'm here to protect you, Navanod. As I've stated before, when we first met, before you ventured to Frostedge, I'm your mentor. I swore to your father that I would teach you the ways of the Ranger, and I would make you into a man. Just because you had a vision does not make you a man. You must complete your Spirit Quest now. Correct? However, you and I can do this after we reach your brothers. I'm sure the news of Stone City will reach them long before our arrival. But seeing you may raise some spirits."

"I don't think so." Navanod said forlornly. "My brothers and I never got along well. I don't think it was because I was clumsy, but something else made them hate me."

"Was?" Gray grinned. "You still are, boy."

Navanod rolled his eyes and continued, "Since they were stronger than me, they picked on me. I was their lesser. They were better at everything, and I'm no good at anything."

"Not true." the Ranger stated. "When I trailed you on your journey, I learned a lot about you, boy. I learned that you are strong-willed, and you have a natural fighting spirit. And while you may be clumsy with that sword," he gestured to the custom sword that Navanod's father, King Ryvax had crafted for him, "you are lithe and swift on your feet. Rangers are not supposed to be large, boy. We are agile, and that is what saves us." He paused for a moment then tapped the side of his skull with his forefinger, "That, and our minds." He grinned. "You will make a good Ranger. You just need training, discipline, and lots of patience. None of which you possess right now." He chuckled.

Navanod smiled lightly and pulled his blanket tighter over his shoulders once again. Minutes of silence passed between the Ranger and the boy. The silence was welcome, but at the same time, it caused Navanod to revisit the horror he had witnessed earlier that day at Stone City. Both his mother and father were killed while he was away. He could never again look upon their faces or say goodnight when the moon rose. He would never again be able to laugh at his father's stupid jokes and behavior, or smell the sweet fragrance of food in the kitchen as he helped his mother prepare dinner. The memories of his family would forever haunt Navanod Taneer Atokad.

A few tears began to fall down the boy's cheeks, and he buried his head in his arms, sobbing silently.

Gray noticed, but did nothing for several moments. When the hiccups began to settle, the Ranger took a deep breath. "Navanod, death comes to all. We all live, and we all die. Some are taken before we believe it is their time, but all things happen for a reason. Yes, your family is gone, but this is not the end just yet. Your father would be proud of you, as would your mother.

You accomplished a great feat by traveling to Frostedge and back. Now you must embark upon another journey.

"This time you know you will not be alone. I'll be there to guide you along the way…again." He allowed a smile to tug at his lips. "I'm here."

Navanod looked upon the Ranger with new eyes. Before, all he saw was an emotionless man without a compassionate bone in his body. Now, as he stared at Gray, he saw a new man, a man that did feel, but accepted death because it was inevitable. Navanod smiled weakly and nodded. He did not see a Ranger sitting before him. He saw a mentor, a friend, a brother, and maybe even a father. For a family is not defined by blood. A family is something much, much more.

*Many things inspire eighteen-year-old **Joseph D. Bryant**: music, Star Wars, his family, and the world around him. In a few more years you can expect to see him teaching Language Arts, raising a family, and publishing books in Montana. Working with 826 Seattle was a "push in the right direction for me. I couldn't be happier."*

I DON'T WANT TO BE KNOWN ONLY AS A BLACK FEMALE, BECAUSE, AS I'VE LEARNED RECENTLY, I'M NOT. WHEN I WALK DOWN THE STREET, PEOPLE DON'T THINK, "HEY, LOOK AT THAT IRISH, BERBIAN, CREOLE, DOMINICAN GIRL." I GUESS SINCE OTHER PEOPLE DON'T SEE THAT, I FEEL THAT I HAVE TO.

-NYESHAYA MCCOY

THE ESSENCE OF FAMILY

Nyeshaya McCoy

No one in the world is fully one ethnicity; everyone is mixed in one way or another. If your skin is white, most likely you have some black inside, and vice versa. Take me for instance; my family is like a huge melting pot with just about every flavor mixed up inside. I was talking to my mom recently and found out about all the different cultures that are in our family. I am African American, Native, Italian, and oh so much more.

It is vital to me that I identify and learn about these traditions and cultures so that I can better understand myself. Statistically, I am African American, which, don't get me wrong, is a good thing. In fact, I feel mostly in my heart to be black and I'm very proud of that. But, I don't want to be known only as a black female, because, as I've learned recently, I'm not. When I walk down the street, people don't think, "Hey, look at that Irish, Berbian, Creole, Dominican girl." I guess since other people don't see that, I feel that I have to.

My greatest grandfather was a black Irish. His family was from the western part of Ireland, just south of Donegal. He and his wife moved to Jefferson, Louisiana. Shortly after, he got a divorce and remarried to a southern Creole woman. They had fourteen children; one of them was my great, great, great, grandmother who wedded a Choctaw Native. Together they had nine kids and took in a Choctaw orphan when she was a baby. They named her Josephina. When she was only fifteen she gave birth to a baby boy. The father of the baby was Dominican and Berbian and he left shortly after the arrival of their son.

My great, great grandfather married and had five children. He named his first daughter Josephina after his mother, who passed away the morning of her granddaughter's birth. The second Josephina married an Italian man named Angelo Selvario. They had nine kids together, one of which was my grandfather. He married my grandmother, a black and Native woman. They had four kids. The third-born was my mother, who gave birth to four daughters and three sons.

I am so proud of the different cultures and backgrounds that are within me. There is so much love and acceptance in my family and I am so appreciative for that. I've been told many stories about how my family had to struggle through poverty and the chauvinistic society they lived in. I've heard about my great uncle going through the Civil Rights movement, my great, great, great grandmother at the Powwows, and even Papa Angel's " little misunderstanding" with the mob. I have seen many pictures, from the Reservation to the little shack in Louisiana.

The people of my past are very intriguing to me; they were strong, united, and inspiring. Even through the times in the world when there wasn't acceptance for people to date let alone wed anyone outside of their race, they still found a way to make things work out for the better.

So there you have it, just some of my family's past. Don't feel bad if you're a little perplexed by this; I get a headache just thinking about it from time to time, but it's who I am and it's who I love.

This whole experience was so enlightening and empowering to me. I feel that I now know and understand myself and my surroundings more evidently. Maybe, in some ways, understanding more about all the different ethnic groups I am part of helps me understand even more why I identify so much with being an African American. That is the culture in which I was raised and the culture that is most strongly in my heart.

I would recommend to anyone who is curious about who he or she is to take some time to look deeper into it and just really connect with it. What can it hurt?

If you don't learn about your past, how do you expect to understand your future?

Friendly, artistic, independent, and intellectual: these are just a few of the words that seventeen-year-old **Nyeshaya McCoy** *uses to describe herself. She loves to draw and is inspired by her family and friends. Her goal is to graduate from high school in June and get a grant for college.*

THIS **TRIP** CHANGED MY

LIFE. MEETING **NEW**

FAMILY GAVE ME A

BETTER SENSE OF **WHO** I

AM, **UNVEILED** A PART OF

MYSELF I **NEVER KNEW**

EXISTED. GETTING BACK

TO MY **NORMAL** EVERYDAY

LIFE WAS GOING TO **HAVE** ITS

PROS AND **CONS**, BUT I

WOULD **NEVER FORGET**

TO **REMEMBER**.

-SCHYLER MISHRA

FORGET TO REMEMBER

Schyler Mishra

When I fell asleep on the plane out of San Francisco, I was in America. I was "Sky, the take-no-prisoners, raging-party guy" who didn't have a care in the world. When I woke up over international waters, I was in the middle of a change unknown to me. I'd left behind all that was familiar and soon we'd reach our final destination, India, where my father was born, and where he, my half-brother, and I were going to participate in our cousin Sanjew's wedding and meet family members my brother and I had never met. I didn't know what it would be like in India. I didn't know that it would feel as if my world was turned upside down. Everything I knew and was comfortable with would be gone. Everything would be written in symbols I could not recognize, as if I could not read. The only thing I recognized and the only people I would be able to communicate with would be my dad and brother. I never had been with them for this long, only seeing them for a weekend at a time.

In the past I didn't rely on my dad for much of anything. When I saw him for a weekend here and there I would just sit in my room and watch television, not really having very much interaction with him. Basically tuning him out when he tried to lecture me about everything he thought he needed to, which was a lot. Now there was no television or door between us, just my dad, brother, and me. I was unsure about how well we would get along together, especially since it was going to be a month. Being taken out of the box, so to speak, forced me to have to actually listen to all my dad had to say. I couldn't just block him out. He knew how to survive in this foreign country. This was where he grew up. Everything from the trains to the hotel, my dad took care of. It was strange having to rely on him to take care of every little detail.

The plane was close to reaching its destination: New Delhi, India. After two long flights I was anxiously awaiting the conclusion of this seemingly never-ending trip. Every mile was a step closer to getting off the oversized sardine can.

I thought I knew what I had gotten myself into, but I honestly had no idea what was in store for me once I stepped off the airplane. This place was nothing I could have imagined; it was humid, crammed full of different colored Indian people, which was kind of scary at first because I had never seen really dark-skinned Indians before. Once we finally made it through the crowd to find the people who were picking us up, something scary caught my eye near the entrance, and a feeling of panic began to overtake me: two men with machine guns by the door. Outside, the first thing I noticed was a distinct odor that I couldn't place, which was hard to get used to.

As we drove, bumping along, the road looked like it had been obliterated by war some time ago. Now this isn't like a road you see in America. This road was beat up, no barriers on the side. Full of holes, looking like it hadn't been paved in the last fifty years, people driving totally erratically, swerving from side to side while honking their horns uncontrollably. A bus pulled up to the right of us about a hundred feet away, a dilapidated bus, with no doors and people so packed in they were literally hanging on by one hand. I saw lots of people riding bikes and walking along the ditch on the side of the road. All kinds of people: workers, men in dress clothes, women in saris, and kids. We stopped at a restaurant. I saw a lot of poor people walking around outside. This girl came up to me and stuck her hand out and muttered in Hindi. I didn't know what she said, but from her putting her hand out I figured she was asking for money. I was perplexed; How could a little girl be walking around alone and barefoot?

At the train station, I was full of fear and constantly looking around me, paranoid that someone would try and rob or shoot me. My dad, brother, and I stood at the entrance of the train station. He was talking to a few men when something started blaring loudly. After a minute I realized no matter how much I listened I wouldn't understand, because it was in another language. We got on the train and soon went to sleep. When we stopped, two men got on the train to pick our bags up. One was Rajase, my dad's cousin, and the second one was my dad's brother, Uncle Law. We got off the train and as we drove through this small town, I noticed that it was not very superior to all the other little towns I had seen along the way. It was just another small town with no modern technology, as I would soon find out. But this was where my dad's side of my family had lived.

Once we arrived at the house where we were staying, I saw it was bigger than all the other buildings around the area. It was made of stone with a metal fence surrounding it, most likely to keep out robbers. It was very late so we decided to go to bed. We had to set up mosquito nets over the beds, which were kind of tricky to set up and maneuver. I was so tired I just drifted off to sleep.

The next day as we were driving to Uncle Law's house, some of the people outside saw me and did a double take, glaring at me. Here I was, a white guy in their eyes, totally smug, wearing Abercrombie & Fitch and shades. I had my headphones on because the driver seemed to think he had to honk his horn every five seconds or the car would explode. As we got close I saw some cows just walking along out of nowhere. I guess they were allowed to wander free, some part of the traditional small-town religious beliefs. When we arrived at Uncle Law's house I was pleasantly surprised by how nice it was. It was no mansion, but it was pretty nice overall, a few bedrooms, a decent-sized television.

My brother and I walked up to the roof and some people were in the midst of a ceremony. We didn't know what was going on at all. A few minutes later Sanjew brought us over to the priest and we sat down in front of him. He was dressed in a robe and was very old and had no teeth. He began to mutter something in Hindi to us, very fast, then rubbed some color and rice on our foreheads and we had to say what he said, which was translated by our cousin. This was the ceremony to become a Brahmin. Sanjew gave us a yellow string to put around our arms, which is a defining Brahmin symbol.

As the trip went on, my brother and I connected, not just as half brothers, but also as friends. Our relationship grew stronger; we talked all the time now. Instead of just listening to our own CD players and ignoring each other, we would hang out, making jokes about the situations we were in or making observational comments. I began to see him in a different light. He wasn't that strange annoying brother I perceived him to be. He was a strong person with very good morals and a huge heart. There now was a bond between us; we weren't two strangers anymore.

The night before the wedding there was a huge celebration, a feast with over two hundred people. All of the family got dressed in their finest clothes. My brother and I put on our Kurta pajamas, which were a traditional set of clothes that my dad had bought us the day before at the tailor's. We piled into the jeep and drove to the park where the feast was held. We took lots of pictures with people and met more friends of the family and watched a traditional ceremony, where we had huge leis of flowers put on us. There was a giant buffet with tons of Indian food.

The next day we all got dressed up once again. This time we wore suits, and some custom turbans that Sanjew gave us, "just for fashion," I remember him saying. At the prewedding site there was a traditional horse to ride for the groom, but my uncle told me to ride it. I was uneasy because the horse had no saddle and I didn't want to be thrown off. As the parade started I was just sitting on the horse, looking around at all the people who were outside of the parade looking in, and all my family and their friends dancing around wildly. People thought I was the groom, but my brother and me were just groomsmen. Finally, we got to the building where the wedding was held, and we were greeted by having colors rubbed on our faces and more flower leis. We were guests of honor so we were escorted everywhere and got full VIP treatment.

We walked down the stairs into a hall with hundreds of chairs, a stage, buffet, and disco floor. We danced for a while, had some food, and then sat on stage and watched the ceremony. When we saw my cousin's bride come on stage we were surprised by what she had on, a full dress lined in gold with twenty-five bracelets on each arm. I looked at my brother and was like, wow, and he looked back and nodded, throwing up an "okay" sign.

Soon after we decided to leave to get some rest. When we got home that night I tried to ignore the permanent ringing in my ears from the constant loud music. Wedding ceremonies last all night in India, so we were woken up at six in the morning to go to the end of it. We crawled out of the mosquito net and got dressed and sat in on the ceremonies. We didn't have a choice because we were the best men. The ceremony was interesting but confusing. Finally we were summoned to the middle of the room where they served us some kind of sweet snack and gave us money inside of traditional envelopes, along with money to the groom, of course. Once this was over everyone headed outside, and my cousin's new wife started to cry as part of the ceremony. They got in the car and that was it, until I saw them later that day.

Two days after the wedding we were leaving Rewa to go to Bombay, which is the New York of India. Once we arrived we went straight to the building where we were staying with my dad's rich friend. He had a very lavish place; to say he was well off was an understatement. As we walked into the penthouse my mouth fell open in awe, and I whistled. This place had money written all over it, marble floors, paintings, carpet, and very tasteful furniture. Our room included a twenty-foot bed Shaquille O'Neal could have slept on and still had space.

Once the week passed I was sad that we had to go. I had gotten so used to the rich life. I didn't want to leave, because I knew it was the life I was destined to live.

We took another long train ride back to Rewa. After the week we spent there it was time to leave for good. I was really emotionally torn up by leaving; I felt I had drawn close to my family. I had only spent a few weeks with them, but it didn't matter because I knew I wouldn't see them for a long time. As we were leaving a few of my family members started crying, which made me try to fight the tears.

We arrived at the train station, which was different than all the other times, because this felt so final. Uncle Law started to tear up and he hugged my brother and my brother said, " I love you." This broke my uncle 'cause he started crying. Then I started crying and hugged him. By far this was the defining moment in the trip. As we left I was still crying. My dad started talking to me about how I had found my family and now had a bond with them, telling me not to forget about them in the future, which I knew I wouldn't.

Before this trip, I had built up a shield between my father and me; it had always been there until now. I lowered the shield on our trip so we were able to communicate for the first time, not just as two people but as father and son. He told stories and we asked him a ton of questions about everything. Meeting his family, seeing where he grew up and how much he overcame gave me a better sense of who he was, and his mentality. I never had any idea of how hard he had it until I went to India. Just us hanging out allowed us to talk about things we never had before, which I think was important in the casual part of our relationship. He was never short on giving me any advice I needed or he thought I needed to know, which now I realized showed how much he cared, and no matter how I acted he never stopped caring. It's too bad it took so long for me to realize this.

On the last leg of our trip, we went to Agra to see the Taj Mahal, which was amazing to see in real life. It was so much more extravagant than I ever imagined it could be. With only one more location to go until we left India, the end was drawing near. We left Agra and went back to New Delhi where we saw sights and shopped. We picked up my dad's wife's daughter and left New Delhi. Flying home, I began to feel sad once again, because I knew once we got off the plane we'd all have to return to our normal everyday lives.

The month I was in India I learned more about it than I did my whole life in America. I was captivated by the art and style of how everything was made, from the clothes to the art and historical buildings. Before, I was never proud of my Indian culture. Now I can say, "I'm Indian and I'm proud!" Gaining this knowledge of India and the experiences really helped me realize and be comfortable with a part of myself I never recognized before.

Seeing India and how so many people live in poverty and will never see or have the things I have really impacted me. It made me thankful for what I have and stop taking for granted all my possessions. I never knew what I had till I had nothing. Even though I wasn't rich by any means, I had more than many in India will ever have. This trip changed my life. Meeting new family gave me a better sense of who I am, unveiled a part of myself I never knew existed. Getting back to my normal everyday life was going to have its pros and cons, but I would never forget to remember.

"In the last 6 months, I have changed my life 180 degrees. I am living proof that change is never impossible to make." This is what nineteen-year-old **Schyler Mishra** would like you to know. He is also inspired by his father, and likes computers, weight lifting, video games, and music. He most likes about himself that he is "friendly and straight to the point."

I FELT REALLY ALONE.
No one could EVER
UNDERSTAND ME AT THE
TIME; EVERYONE WAS TOO
SPACED OUT AND CAUGHT
UP IN THEMSELVES AND
EVERYTHING THEY HAD TO
DO. I ALWAYS FELT LIKE I
WAS A MOUSE IN A ROOM
WITH A LOT OF SNAKES, OR
LIKE A KID WHO HAS TO HIDE
UNDER HER BED BECAUSE SHE
IS AFRAID OF THE DARK
AND NO ONE IS AROUND TO
GUIDE HER.

-LIERA WILLIAMS

WHEN WILL WE GET THERE

Liera Williams

I come from a big family of fourteen. This includes my two younger sisters and three older sisters, my two brothers, my parents, my three little nephews, and, last but not least, my two-year-old niece. My family has had a lot of problems to over-come. We had to do so many things to stay together. So much pain, hurt, and trouble ran through the family. It was too much to handle, too much to go through. It made me want to run away because I couldn't take all of what was going on. We all had our ups and downs, but we still stayed together because everyone was able to put a part in it. We had to know when it was time to be serious, like when another problem came upon us. Even though we all struggled, we all strived to stay in school and my parents tried their hardest to keep working.

Unfortunately my parents had to quit working, so my family was not financially stable. We just started to lose everything, slowly but surely. Since my parents weren't able to make enough money, at one point we had to give up our house and we were homeless. That made me and all of my sisters and brothers very hurt and sad. We felt like our world was coming to an end. We knew then that we really had to work together to survive. We all knew that this was a journey that we didn't want to ever take again. We were actually homeless before about eight years ago. We never thought that we would have to go through that again. At first my mom was just going to make us all move back to Kansas City, but she was not prepared for that, so we went to live with my aunty in the city next to ours. While we stayed with her life was very hard. The neighborhood was very bad out there and my mom was watching over us as much as she could. She was so scared that we would end up doing drugs or something else bad like everyone else out there. We didn't really have that much freedom because my mom made us come in the house really early since things started to pop off as soon as nighttime would hit. People would start shooting, fighting, drinking, and smoking, bringing the police there every single night.

After a while, it was getting too hard because seventeen of us were living in a two-bedroom apartment, including my aunt and her two sons. There was barely anywhere for anyone to sleep, and people came in and out of that house selling weed and just doing it all. I never really felt safe in that environment. I always sat alone in the house with my sister; I felt she was the only person I had. I felt really alone. No one could ever understand me at the time; everyone was too spaced out and caught up in themselves and everything they had to do. I always felt like I was a mouse in a room with a lot of snakes, or like a kid who has to hide under her bed because she is afraid of the dark and no one is around to guide her.

When we weren't able to live with my aunt anymore, we moved into a shelter that was not that satisfying, but it was somewhere to live. It was very small; it had one small room with seven of us living in it. My older sisters and brother did not move there with us; they wanted to go out on their own. I

was so sad after that, because it was bad enough that we had lost
our house; now losing my sisters and my older brother made it
worse.

I no longer wanted to stay with my parents anymore; I just
wanted to run away and find my sisters and bring them back
with me. My family just fell apart. We all departed from each
other. Everyone argued because we were so tired of being
clamped in together. We had to follow the rules of other adults;
there was a specific time when we had to eat and leave and come
back. It was very hard waking up at seven a.m. and then having
to be in your room by nine p.m. I wanted to go crazy, because
if I was doing something outside of the shelter, I would have to
stop and be back by nine p.m. It was horrible because the people
who were managers of the shelter did an inspection every night
just to see if everyone was in the room.

As time went on, it was our time to move, and we didn't
quite have a place to stay, so we moved to this other shelter that
had two bedrooms in it. It had more room than the other place,
but still I did not feel like I had all the space I needed. I had a
hard time staying focused in school because we had to move so
much. The district made us switch schools because we moved
out of our original school district. We then moved into this other
shelter that was more like transitional housing; we had three
rooms and our own kitchen, but we had a limited time to live
there. I felt more like I was at home; I still had the feeling of
having to move, but I felt more comfortable.

From there, we then moved to Renton. (We had already lived
in all the shelters in Tacoma.) I had to get out of my school
because I couldn't make it to and from there every day. I really
did not want to move to Renton because I didn't know anyone
there; Tacoma was where all my friends were. Besides losing my
school, I also had to give up going to my church and visiting my
sisters as much as I used to. The shelter in Renton let us stay for
three to four months. It was very relaxing at times, and I got into
a school out there. My sisters came to visit us every two or three
weeks.

We then moved to Seattle, where we stayed in a shelter that
was very dirty. It was nothing like I planned it to be. It had holes

in the walls and a lot of stains on the floors; we even had rats and little mice. I felt like I could have just lived outside and made a better life. I tried to be away from there as much as I could, so when I got home from school I would always go to the youth center. We could have lived there for three months but my mom was not feeling it, so we stayed there for a little less than a month.

Once again, I was so tired of having to pack up and move. I always tried to make myself believe that this was THE LAST TIME, but it never was. I knew that there was always more to come. We really couldn't find anywhere to go in Seattle so we moved to Kent, where we stayed in a transitional house for three months. I felt pretty safe; there was no fighting or incidents that caused the police to be there every night. It was way better than the environment where my aunty lived. We were going to school in Seattle so we caught a cab to and from school everyday. At first it was kind of embarrassing, but then I realized that it was just another solution to keep me from having to switch schools again.

When our time was up there we then moved back to Seattle where we stayed in another transitional house. My mom told me that we would have our own place after this but I was kind of confused. I didn't know if I should believe her or not! I didn't really know what to believe at that point. I did end up switching schools again, but this time it was by choice, not by force. We lived there for the longest, which was about six months.
I thought we were never going to get our own place and that we were going to live in shelters our whole life. Every day before I went to sleep I prayed because I wanted to be like most other families and have my own place. I thought it would make the rest of my family and me happier. Maybe it would bring us closer, maybe it wouldn't, but I really wanted to find out.
After the sixth months that we lived there, my mom went out searching for an apartment, and my dad started to work. Whenever they returned home I always asked if there was any luck; none at first, but they had no time to give up yet. We could just feel that something good was coming near.

Before I knew it, my mom said that we got an apartment, but

it was not ready for us to move in yet. I got so happy; no one knew how happy I was and words just couldn't explain. Our time was up at the other place so we moved to this hotel until it was time for us to move to the apartment. We were just trying to do anything to keep our spirits up; we were just happy that we got to move into our own place. We stayed in the hotel for three weeks. It went pretty fast and easy, and I felt happy the whole way through because I knew my problem would be solved in a few weeks.

That third week our apartment was ready for us. We got all settled in and fixed up our house. While being homeless I switched schools seven times in one year. I hope that I am now in a school where I will remain until I graduate next year.

While we were homeless it was very stressful, so I really did not want to attend school, and I just skipped school almost every day so I would not have to be around a lot of people. The other students just really bothered me. They acted like everything was all perfect in their lives and like they didn't need help from anyone. I was getting bad grades in school and failing all of my classes. It kind of makes you feel like you are not wanted any-where.

This was one of our family's biggest struggles that we've had yet. It was obviously big enough to run my older siblings away. Being so young, I wasn't able to do that so I had to live with it. It was something that I would never want to experience again. It cost way too much, it caused me to fall behind in school, it caused me to lose all of my friends, it caused me to be a very self-centered person who just wanted to be all alone, and it also caused me to lose something very close to me: MY FAMILY.

Everybody that has never been homeless before is so lucky because being homeless is not something that they would want to experience. They should know that what they have as far as living is way better than any environment that I lived in.

Now that we are not homeless anymore, my family is very close to each other. We all have the space that we need and we can give each other privacy. My older brother moved back in with us. My three older sisters come and visit us more often, like every other weekend. Both of my parents have good jobs and they make enough money to support everyone in the house. All of my younger siblings, including me, attend school on a daily basis and we all get better grades. I am just so happy that we were able to overcome that and now we live peacefully.

*Seventeen-year-old **Liera Williams** hopes to one day become a psychiatrist. As she works toward her goal, she is inspired by God, her parents, and her sisters. She can also be found playing instruments, singing, and dancing.*

MOST OF ALL, THE BIGGEST

INSPIRATION IN MY LIFE IS

MY FATHER, THE MAN WHO

SAID, "LOOK FORWARD,

NOT BACK, YOU CAN BE

WHATEVER YOUR MIND

AND HEART TELL YOU THAT

YOU CAN BE." I LOVE

YOU AND I MISS YOU.

RIP, DENNIS ROBINSON.

-VINCENT ROBINSON

Look Forward, Not Back

Vincent Robinson

My history of playing football comes from my father, who was always a Bears fan, and it got passed on to me, just seeing him every Sunday wake up to watch the Bears get beat or win; it did not matter, it was just a game, and he loved it as much as I did. He told me stories about the great running back Gale Sayers, in my point of view the best running back to ever play for the Bears. His style of running, blocking, and most of all, hitting the hole, was skillful and amazing. He played six years without getting hurt, and set records. A year later he got hurt when he rolled his leg, but the next season he came back and broke all of the records that he set the previous six years.

Gale Sayers was my favorite player, but I would love to run like Walter Payton, who was called Sweetness, the greatest runner to

ever play the game. He could shake you, run you over, stiff-arm
you, you name it, he could do it. He was also a great man on and
off the field: a family man, a community man, and a great inspiration. That's why I respect him so much; but no player will ever be
better than Gale Sayers.

I'm from Seattle, Washington. I'm seventeen years old. In
fourth grade I moved to Las Vegas. That is when I started to love
football, because every day on the playground with the other kids I
would shake them, stiff-arm them, but not run them over because I
was not ready. I was still small, but I was the best. So I played Little
League and I was unstoppable. No one wanted to see me on the
field. Kids were like, "You're going somewhere in life."

I said, "Just don't guess my future. It's not the only game I play."

They said, "Like what?"

"I play basketball, run track, and play baseball."

Then after a year in Las Vegas back to Seattle I went. I got back
to Seattle ready to play on a team. So I did. I was one of the best
on the team. I started in Little League until seventh grade. I played
junior high football at Meeker. I started in seventh and eighth
grade, both seasons. They were not good, but I gave my best effort
every year.

Then came ninth grade. A big year, ninth grade. I played for the
Kent Knights. That year I played quarterback. I was the best in the
league that year. I had like two touchdowns per game; maybe, if I
was lucky, I would pull off three. That feeling of playing that year
was so good. I had like twenty-two touchdowns: eighteen touchdowns I put in myself and four passes to four different receivers.
We did not pass that much because our passing game was not that
good. We ran mostly, running plays and reverses. Both of our running backs were nice. One had thirty touchdowns and the other
had twenty-six. We were the nicest players on the team. We had an
undefeated year, but we got knocked out of the playoffs.

Now I play for the Cleveland High School Eagles. The Head
coach, Keywon, is a good head coach. Players like him as well as
his coaching staff. Any problem goes to Coach Keywon. Now
about the players. Here's last year's lineup: quarterback Dawon;
fullback Nick; running backs me and D Reed, Justin and Greg;
wide receivers D Heart, Chris, and Tony Whitehead.

On this team most of the guys are standout players. They play with heart, but the main receiver dropped six passes in an important game; we needed it to go to the playoffs. The coach didn't play me that much that game. It hurt because I know I could have made a difference. I played running back for four years, but I came to a team that at that time did not treat me like a family, so I made a difference by myself by yelling and keeping everybody's spirits up. We play as a family, we win as a family. We don't need one person trying to be an outcast; he might be a damn good football player, but that's not going to win us games. One person does not make a team, a family makes a team. On my old football team, everybody had fun playing because we stuck together and did not worry about anyone making a mistake.

When I first came to Cleveland, D Reed, who is also a tailback, sized me up and was like, "What position do you play?" I said, "Tailback," and he was like, okay, is this guy going to take my position? When I got my pads and started practicing, he was like checking out my style of running, and what he saw was determination, because I don't give up, and he saw some things that I can improve on. When I would mess up on something he would pull me aside in practice and tell me what I should do and how I should run it. Ever since then I've been looking up to him. When he runs, it inspires me to run like him because he's quick. He has the shakes like Gale Sayers and the heart of Sweetness, but he's not really a running back to run you over, he's more of a speedy one to get past you. That's a style I'm working on, but I'm also working on running over you and staying low, my motion of running and my style.

D Reed also taught me how to pass block and how to go out of the backfield and catch the ball. He just says, "Look in front of you and check out who's in front of you when the ball's in the air. If it's clear or not clear, catch the ball. If there's a defender in front of you, do what you can: run over them, stiff-arm them, or shake them. Do what you can to get positive yards."

Me and D Reed run the field before games to get used to it. We help one another work out so when game time rolls around, we're both ready. When we're not playing football, we're usually hanging out like family. In fact, later on that season we were hanging out one night and went to one of my cousin's houses. I went in the house and everybody said hello to D Reed, and I saw his picture on the wall. That night we found out we were cousins. That was so crazy, it never happened to me before. Now when we're around one another we know we are safe, because I got his back and he has mine.

So, what does my future hold? I want to go to business school for restaurant management, because I like eating soul food. But owning a business, you need a team. Once I learn how to make a team through football, then I'll know I'll be ready to take that into business.

Playing for Coach Keywon inspired me to go for what I want in life, like a nice car, big house, and most of all a family. Someone to go home to and kiss your kids and tell them you love them. Two other people who inspired me were Gale and Walter, because of how they carried themselves on and off the field and how they gave back to their communities.

Most of all, the biggest inspiration in my life is my father, the man who said, "Look forward, not back, you can be whatever your mind and heart tell you that you can be." I love you and I miss you.

RIP, Dennis Robinson.

*Legendary football players Gale Sayers and Walter Payton may be seventeen-year-old **Vincent Robinson's** inspirations, but his goal is to go into business management. His hobbies are working out and playing sports. And being a good sports player is what Vincent likes most about himself.*

WE ALL feel the need to BELONG, to FEEL like we're PART of something. Having GOOD FRIENDS helps you FIND yourself, and HELPS you GROW UP.

-Ryan McFadden

FOREVER FRIENDS

Ryan McFadden

F amily is indefinable. Family is love. Family is acceptance.
Family makes you feel like you belong to something important, like you're part of something. Sometimes, family isn't really
family, but really good friends. My closest friends are the most
important part of my life. I can tell them anything, things that I
could never tell my family. Not every friend falls under this cat-
egory, though. I have many friends, but only two are close. Never
in my life have I found any friends that have become as close to me
as Matt and Emily.

   We met at Marshall last year, and when I first met them, I knew
that we would become good friends. At first, we were just buddies
in a group of friends, kind of similar to the show Friends, which
is funny, because we all watched it. At one time, we were going to

remake a couple of episodes, and we had scripts and everything. There was me, Dyare, Matt, Emily, Mike, Wells, Jordan, and Kasia. Jordan and Kasia are no longer part of our "group." Jordan made a few mistakes, because of his immaturity, and Kasia turned out to be untrustworthy. Dyare moved to Las Vegas, and Mike moved to California. Even though our group is no longer completely together, we developed a powerful bond. All of us had a place; we all just fit in together. I fell in love with Dyare (still am, as a matter of fact), and Matt and Emily became boyfriend and girlfriend, and even though they have had problems, they are still together and probably will get married.

I think we all grew up fast, which has its benefits, but also has some drawbacks. Instead of going and partying and getting into trouble, we usually just stay at Matt's and hang out. We always seem to have the most fun when it's just the three of us, because we feel comfortable with each other.

One day, Matt came up to me and said, "Do you realize how old we are? Like, we're young, but we're so much older than the people who are our age. We just seem to understand things." It's true, and though we still have a little bit to go, we are pretty mature for our age. We goof off a lot, and some people think we're immature, but we aren't; we're just having fun. I'm the oldest, being eighteen, but sometimes I feel like I'm the youngest, because Matt and Emily have been through a lot more than I have. One had a bad addiction at a young age, because of relatives, but luckily was able to break it. Another had an abusive stepfather. We all came from different backgrounds, but we've all had similar experiences, and we are a lot alike in our behaviors, personalities, attitudes, and views. I think that is why we get along so well.

Since Dyare moved down to Vegas, Matt and Emily and I have become even closer. We see each other every weekend and sometimes during the week, and we always have a lot of fun when we are together. I don't think I've ever had a day with them that hasn't been fun, where we haven't done something completely stupid. One day, for example, I was riding Matt's BMX bike, which had loose handlebars. I knew this, but I decided to ride anyway. As I was riding, there was a jump in front of me. I jumped it, and when I came down, the handlebars flipped forward and over the front I

went. Luckily, when I fell I landed in the grass, but this is the type
of dumb stuff that we always do. We always work out together, too,
and Matt has taught me a lot of things about fighting that I never
knew.

I know for a fact that we will all be friends forever. We made an
oath to never let anything come between us. We also plan to get an
apartment together. When you do as much as the three of us have
done together, you develop a family-like bond. I am so glad that I
found friends like these, and I am lucky to have people that care
and look out for me. It is comforting to know that if I need anything, any time, or if I need to tell someone my problems, I can go
to Emily and Matt.

Friendship is a very important thing. It is vital in growing up.
It's also nice to have people that you can relate to and tell things to,
and have fun with. We all feel the need to belong, to feel like we're
part of something. Having good friends helps you find yourself,
and helps you grow up. Finding friends that you would trust your
life with is very special. I love my friends. They are my family. And
no matter what happens, even when you have nothing else, your
family will always be there for you.

*A lot of people may think that eighteen-year-old **Ryan McFadden** is weird, he says, but he's not. He's just funny, intelligent, outgoing, and deep. He is inspired by "anyone who makes it," especially his little brothers and friends. On his way to becoming a guitarist, you can find Ryan playing guitar, going to raves, and lifting weights.*

My UNCLE J. WAS A THUG. THAT'S HOW I WOULD DESCRIBE HIM. I MEAN, HE WASN'T THE POPE OR NOTHING. UNCLE J. DID WHAT WAS GOING TO MAKE THE MONEY TO FEED HIS KIDS AND KEEP THEM IN DECENT CLOTHES.

-RAYMOND WILFORD

My Uncle J. (Julius)

Raymond Wilford

My uncle J. (Julius) was my role model. He was how an uncle was supposed to be. You know, the person who lets you get away with the things that your parents won't, like if you slip and say a curse word, he would tell you that you shouldn't curse. But he understood that boys will be boys and the only way boys will learn is by experiencing things like girls, school, and trying to be a man even when you are not ready for the responsibilities that men have to deal with. Take bills, for example: How can you be a man if you don't pay your own bills? He was the type of man who would have told you about it, but he would also let you experience life yourself. I really miss my uncle. He was killed in 1998. I was eight years old. It didn't hit me that he was really gone until his funeral. I seen my whole family crying, and then it hit me: My uncle is really gone, and he's not coming back.

My uncle J. was a thug. That's how I would describe him. I mean, he wasn't the pope or nothing. Uncle J. did what was going to make the money to feed his kids and keep them in decent clothes. From what I know, he did what he had to, even if that meant selling drugs and robbing people who were basically showing off all their money, like buying fancy cars, rims, expensive jewels and clothes. Where I'm from, we call them stunners, and if someone's stomach is growling, a stunner will get robbed, and a robber won't hesitate to kill you if you don't give everything willingly.

Uncle J. did his wrongs and his rights, but he was still a good person, because he cared about family. If you asked him for something, he would try his best to get it for you. My uncle also helped his friends, and friends are the ones who killed him in the end. When his friends were in trouble, he was always the first to step up. He had a hard time getting a job, because of an auto theft when he was only eighteen years old. That changed his life forever. In fact, stealing that car ended his life in a way, now that I think about it. He had a girlfriend and two kids. He had just asked his girlfriend to marry him right before he was killed. I liked his kids, Julius and Jayontay. I love them to this day, because they're all that's left of him and I'd do anything for them if they asked me to, just because they're my uncle's family. Both of his kids were little when he left, and they didn't really understand that Daddy was gone and not coming back. From what I remember, his son didn't cry. I think that was because my uncle always used to tell him to stop crying, so he just didn't cry. His daughter, on the other hand, did end up crying, but I think that was because her mother was crying and holding both of them real close. So my guess is that she was sad because her mother was sad. His daughter has long soft looking hair, and she's a beautiful light brown color. She got her skin from her mom, who was also beautiful like that, and Jayontay was shy last time I saw her. His son has short curly hair, which he got from his mom, and he was more my uncle's color, who was on the dark side of brown

Even though my uncle did illegal things, he kept his kids in school, making good grades, and they never knew what he was doing. My uncle had them wanting to be successful in life, so they didn't know anything about drugs or anything like that. My uncle J. would be real nice and loving like to his daughter, but the way boys are raised in my family is rough. If you get mad because you lost a game, you get beat up, but it's always love. If you don't get beat up, then it means Uncle J., Uncle Steven, and any other uncle or cousins don't like you. If you get beat up, that means you are loved and cared for. I think that's what you call tough love.

Uncle J. taught me things my dad would have thought twice about. Like if you saw him drinking and he saw you looking, he would let you have some, but he'd only do it once. He told me that he'd rather me experience drinking with him than have me go into the streets and have something happen to me. So instead of him arguing with me, he'd just say "OK." I learned a lot of things from him. He taught me how to shoot a gun and how to aim. He taught me how to never back down from nobody; all of my uncles taught me that, actually. I was raised like that, and my uncle Julius was a big part of raising me. He also taught me that you should always watch your surroundings, like the people and the area. He didn't actually tell me that, but it became clear when his friends turned on him.

How he died was not peaceful. There were three people involved. They called him at home, because he was friends with them. They told him to meet them at the corner store. Then it seems that they took him to a wooded area, and that's where they shot him in the head, burned his body, and put him under a dumpster. I guess they didn't think anyone would find him there.

My uncle made some bad decisions in his life, but he never was a bad person or a bad parent. He loved his whole family, did good by his kids, his girlfriend, and all the rest of the big family. And he definitely did good by me, his nephew. He taught me a lesson in life: You can't trust everybody who's acting like your friend, so watch everybody you know.

"Keep your family close but enemies closer."

Solid. That is how seventeen-year-old **Raymond Wilford** *would describe himself. He likes the way that he was raised and is inspired by his uncles. You can find him playing football or video games, and after he graduates from high school he would like to attend college and get a degree in "something that's helpful."*

I **FEEL** LIKE I'M A **PRISONER** IN MY **OWN** **HOUSE** WITH **NOWHERE** TO GO AND **NOTHING** TO DO.

-TIARRA KNOX

THE FAMILY
WE WERE GIVEN

Tiarra Knox

M y family is very important to me–every single last one of
them. I love them all, each one for a different reason. They
are my support line to life even if I can't always show it. They irri-
tate me more than I am willing to admit, but I love them nonetheless. I would be lost without them in my life.

There are days when I just want to be alone and shut the world
out. My family sees it as me being evil, but that's not the case.
When I don't feel like being bothered with anyone I just isolate
myself from everything. I don't know how to open up to them and
tell them how I feel. Even if I could open up to them I probably
wouldn't because they run their mouths too much for me, meaning
if I tell them something, the whole family is going to end up finding out. So to keep my business from spreading around I just don't

tell them anything. I feel like I'm a prisoner in my own house with nowhere to go and nothing to do. I have all this time on my hands and nothing to do with it.

Sometimes I wish I could just trade places with no one in particular so he or she could feel my pain and see what I have to go through on a daily basis. When things seem like they are getting too rough for me to handle, when I just can't take it anymore, when I need to get away from everything that I'm going through, I run straight to my aunt's house. There I can be a little kid again, whereas if I'm at home, I feel like I'm a mom who has been robbed of her teenage years. I feel like this all the time because there is no mother figure in my little brother and sister's life. I'm the closest thing they have to a mom, plus my dad puts pressure on me when it comes to my seven-year-old sister. She is like my child I didn't birth. I have to do everything for her and it's starting to take a toll on me. It's like she is grown but she isn't, she talks back to me, gets attitudes, she's just helpless. Sometimes it makes me wonder where my dad, brother, and sister would be without me. I'm their backbone.

My aunt has two daughters my age. They are like the sisters I always wanted but never received. My cousin Alice, who is seventeen, is one of my favorite relatives because we relate to each other so well. It's like she feels the pain I feel, and knows when something is bothering me. Alice is my soulmate. She's about 5' 9", 135, and kind of dark-skinned like the sun has kissed her. She is very intellectual and poetic. She wears braces, has average length hair, very long model-type legs. She has a beautiful personality when she isn't mad at anyone. There are not enough words in the entire world to describe her. She is beautiful inside and out. She is a very caring, loving, funny goofball who loves to have fun. She is also a very good dancer. It's like she speaks a whole different language with her body when she dances.

She knows me better than I know myself. I could sit up with her for hours just talking about how I feel and what's going on in my life. She is my best friend in the whole world. I trust her with my life. She helped me change my outlook on life and how I was living it. If it weren't for Alice I wouldn't be in school getting As and Bs. I'd probably be in the streets selling drugs, living dangerously and hurting loved ones. Just her doing well in school and making the right decisions was enough for me to do the same thing. I have always looked up to her; she brought things out of me that I never knew I could do—such as writing. She keeps me on the right track when I feel like losing it by making me think about the consequences of my actions, and how they will affect me in the long run. It's true that I hear what Alice tells me all the time from the grown-ups in my life, but it's a lot different hearing it from someone my age who knows how I feel, what I have been through, and what I'm going through now. Alice knows and gets me better than anyone else, she knows when I want to be left alone, and she knows when I need love.

I look up to Alice because she has set goals for herself. She is doing something with her life, and is determined to be more than her mom and dad. She's not going to be one of those statistics you hear about—having babies she can't take care of, sleeping with countless men who don't care anything about her. She's not going to end up with a dead-end job, two kids, no babies' father, no car, no house, and no financial support. Her goals are to get in to college and become a writer or a psychologist. She also wants to make her family proud, something she has already accomplished with me. She just recently got a Bill Gates Scholarship that allows her to attend college in Washington state for the first year then after that she can go anywhere she desires for the last three. She is planning on going to the University of Washington for the first year.

I'm sad she is leaving me but I also know she deserves it. I feel that when she leaves she is going to be taking a part of me with her. She has worked very hard to get where she is. This is one of the main reasons why she is my role model. She is following her dreams and goals, even when it gets rough, and when she wants to give up she doesn't. She is my motivation, my inspiration.

I care about her opinion, and how she feels about situations that I'm in. I have to hear her thoughts on things because it matters to me that much. Her opinion matters the most to me because she's not going to tell me something I want to hear, she's going to tell me what she really thinks regardless of my feelings. She gives me good advice and has a lot of wisdom for her age. The things she says to me sound like they are coming from an elder person like a grandmother figure or something. It's like she has been on this earth before and sees things through elderly eyes. Also she's my right-hand man, and even if she's wrong I'm going to listen to what she has to say. I may not use it but I listen nonetheless. I never had to be someone I wasn't around her, which took me nine-and-a-half years to figure out. The reason it took me so long is because I was spending all this time trying to prove to her I was someone I wasn't. I thought if she saw me as a cool, hard person then she would re-spect me. I then realized I never had to be someone I wasn't around her but myself, and she accepted me for who I was and who I am.

The number-one example I can give of how Alice helps me through all my drama is that on Wednesday I had a very bad day. I mean, nothing went my way at all. For starters my dad was sup-posed to pay me that day for help watching my brother and sister while he went to work and didn't, then I had my school picture retaken and what a big mistake that was. I should have just stuck with the original one because this one looks so ugly.

I was also having trouble writing an essay. I praise writers because this thing is harder than it seems. You have to have a lot of patience and great passion. I was so ready to give up, but my teacher wouldn't let me (I so don't like her right now) but anyway she kept pushing me like she was trying to get more out of me when I didn't have any more to give. When I was really about to lose it, Alice and I talked about how I was feeling. She told me that this was just a challenge and I had to push through it in order to come out on top and a winner. She said I can't always give up and punk out on things when they get a little hard because if I do then I would be doing that for the rest of my life. I still didn't want to do it but there was a lot of truth in her words. I wouldn't be hurting anyone but myself if I quit when I was so close to finishing. God, I hate her so much when she is right, it gets on my last nerve.

Alice is part of the extended family I was given. Sometimes I don't like my family, sometimes we don't get along, but when the lights go out we are still a family and that's not going to change. We fuss, fight, just like any other normal family, but I love them with all my heart. I may not like half (more like all) of them, but this is the only family I've known for sixteen-and-a-half years. They love and accept me for who I am. Even though I couldn't ask for a more annoying family, this is the family I was given.

*Sixteen-year-old **Tiarra Knox**
hopes to become a pediatrician
one day. Until then you can find
her singing, dancing, reading, and
writing. Her cousin Alice, her little
brothers, her sister, and her friends
inspire her. What does Tiarra like
most about herself? "My smile,
personality, my eyes, my bottom lip,
and my skin color."*

WHEN I **FIRST** GOT TO MY **PARENTS'** HOUSE, I **WONDERED**, WHAT IF THEY **DON'T WANT ME** HERE? MY **HEART** WAS IN **PAIN**, BUT **NOT PHYSICAL** PAIN. IT WAS THE **EMOTIONAL** PAIN OF **FEARING** THAT THEY WOULDN'T **ACCEPT ME** OR MAYBE THAT I **WAS THERE** JUST **FOR** A **TAX DEDUCTION**.

-AMANDA WEINERT

Strangers? I Think Not

Amanda Weinert

They are the ones who give us hugs
    They are the ones who make us feel special
the way we are
They are the ones who dry our eyes
    when we cry
They are the ones who help us
    when we fall
They are the ones we run to when we are scared
They are the ones put here on this place
    that we call earth to embarrass us
They are the ones who punish us when we
    have done wrong
They are the ones we go to for help

They are the ones who we hurt with our anger
They are the ones who we say we hate
They are the ones who support our choices in life
   right or wrong
They are the ones right there
   cheering on the sidelines
They are so much more than we make them out
   to be
They are most of all who we love despite what we say
   or what they do
They are the ones we are proud
   to call mother and father
They are the ones we can always depend on
   to be there for us no matter what.

I am fifteen and very unsure about this world. I have long dark brown hair; I love country, oldies, and rock music. My favorite rock band is Guns N' Roses. Since I've moved back in with my stepdad and mom I have changed and continue to change. This is what I've learned: Life is rude and has a strange way of doing unexpected things that can have the smallest or the biggest impact on our lives. But life also has its own funny little way of taking care of the ones that live it.

When my mom was younger, she lived on Vashon Island and was always the runt in her group of friends. She would be picked on and made fun of. One day when she was about in the third grade, this boy was following her and bugging her on her way home because he wanted a kiss from her. My mom was too little to be interested in boys. The boy got in front of her and then tried to kiss her. She punched him in the face and pushed him down into some sticker bushes and ran home.

I like boys and don't need self-defense lessons, but it dawned on me: I have a similar story. When I was in fourth grade, I hit a boy in the face because he was dared to hug me by some other boys and I did not want a hug. I just wanted to play football with them!

My mom is short with long dark hair. She is a fighter. She should never be underestimated just because of her size. She's a tough mama.

My mom and me look alike, like the same type of music, and are tough—but I'm not as tough as my mom is yet. We have differences, too, like she thinks my stepdad is cute and I think my stepdad is ugly. She can't play the flute or guitar, and I can.

I feel we are close, but not as close as she is with my little sisters, which bothers me a lot, and not as close as if I had lived with her all my life. This has a big effect on my life because I am afraid to get really close to someone like my mom or dad for fear that just as I am getting used to them being there and start opening up to them all the way, they will just leave me or disappear. I am also afraid that they might think less of me for opening up or just plain won't care. All my life I would start to get close to someone or used to having him or her around, open up, and then never see them again. If I did see them again then it was not the same: They would treat me totally differently and seem to not care about me anymore, like I had some disease or something. When I started to open up to my uncle Roy, I told him everything and felt like we were real close; we did so many things together. Then one day he just started to be rude to me and wouldn't talk to me.

When I was a baby, there was a big court battle between my mom and grandmother over who would get to have my sister, brother, and me. Why would my grandma do this? It feels like we were taken without any consideration of the effect it would have on us in the long run. My mom didn't have enough money to afford a better lawyer than my grandma, so the county gave us to my grandma, which was sad.

About a year ago, my grandma and I weren't getting along, and I went to live with my mom and stepdad. It was really hard because I knew absolutely nothing about them. I had lived with my grandma almost all my life, and the only contact I had with my mom was off and on; she'd be around a week, then disappear off into her own little world. Moving in with my mom was all my mom's idea. When she signed the papers and took it to court, my grandmother was in pure shock that something like this could happen without her say.

I used to have problems, problems I thought that no one would want to sit down and listen to. I used to be so angry at kids who were spoiled and treated their parents like complete crap. To me, parents were a treat and a special privilege to have because I did not know mine as well as I wanted to or live with them. My anger was starting to get the best of me. The anger would drive me so crazy, I would do things that I regret.

My stepdad's name is Greg but I call him Dad. He is a real stand-up comedian; he is always making jokes, trying to make people laugh. He will say whatever is on his mind without hesitation. He is real tall and loves his job at the shipyards. His hair is kind of long, coming about to the halfway point of his ears. He may not be my biological dad, but I still love him as if he were. I have always wanted to meet my biological dad, but he is nowhere to be found. So I have come to call my stepdad Dad. He is there for me when he can be, even though he doesn't have to be. We are sort of close, but not as close as I would like.

There is no way to make up the time that was lost over the years, but with each day I learn something new about my mom and dad. I learn things about my parents I never, ever would have thought they would have done. My dad told me that one time when he was younger he accidentally set his room on fire because he was playing with matches. This story confused me so much; it was just so unexpected. My dad would never do anything like set something on fire. At first, the only thing I could think about was why he was telling me this story; I am never going to set anything on fire. I am just now learning that people can tell me stories and not mean them as lessons for me. My grandmother always told me stories meant to be lessons for me at the end.

When I first got to my parents' house, I wondered, what if they don't want me here? My heart was in pain, but not physical pain. It was the emotional pain of fearing that they wouldn't accept me or maybe that I was there just for a tax deduction. Would they love me or care about me as much as they did my sisters? Even though my stepsister Felicia lives with her mom, I know my dad loves her more than anything, and I wondered if he would ever love me as much as he loves her. I wondered if my mom and I would ever be as close as she is with my half-sister Courtney. She lives with her dad, but she has had more communication over the years with my mom then I have.

When we first pulled up to the house, my stomach was in

knots. The door seemed to be so far away from where it really was. I followed my parents cautiously and slowly. I couldn't believe it. I was actually going to see the house that I had dreamed of all my life up until then. I felt dizzy and totally unsure of what was going to happen next. The door seemed to take forever to open. The first thing I noticed was a sweet odor that filled the air. The odor was something that I could not name, but it reassured me that everything was going to be okay.

Wow! I could not believe my eyes. It was like I was going into a hospital, the house was so clean and tidy. I was afraid to step another foot in the door for fear I was going to mess the house up. Everything had its own place and was neatly set in it. There was no visible sign that someone lived there except for two cats curled up by the window sound asleep.

After an hour or two at their house I was still a little uneasy. They gave me a tour and showed me my sister's room where I was going to stay. The first thing that came into my mind was "Oh God, please help me!" It was so ugly. It looked like somebody had gone and puked Barbie up all over it. There were two beds in the corner covered in girly-girl sheets—white with flowers and but-terflies, pink, yellow, and purple. A toy kitchen neatly sat in the corner. A Barbie alarm clock and a little nightlight were plugged into the wall.

Then my parents went on about their own business. So I sat and watched the cats play. After a while my mom came in the room and asked me what I wanted for dinner. I said I didn't know, and, bam, I was hit with all these choices. I still wasn't sure, so my mom nodded at me, smiled, and was off to the kitchen. Just as soon as she left my dad came out, sat down, and just watched TV. I couldn't help but stare at him; it was only the third or fourth time I'd seen him. I never had talked to him before. I think that he was unhappy or something at the time, but I'm not sure. Believe it or not, my dad and me had our first conversation about a month after I moved in with them. He only seems to have conversations with me when it's just him and me. But it's nice because he often helps me out with problems and questions, and it makes me feel like we are getting the chance to know each other better.

Even though they were so nice to me, I felt I might never get the chance to be close with them like they are with my younger sisters, especially when my sisters were staying at the house. They know my parents better than I do. All I could think about was how do I fit in with them as a family member, what part do I play here in this big house with them? They are complete strangers to me.

I had an anger inside of me toward my mom for letting me be taken, and for not having the chance to be able to grow up with my parents and form that bond that little kids form with their parents that lasts for the rest of their lives. Why do I have to be doing this now, why did this have to happen?

> Living in this house with two complete strangers
> both so totally opposite of me
> Living here where everyone knows everyone but me
> Always having a feeling of them not wanting me in their
>   house
> with them as a part of their lives
> I feel I will never be good enough for them
> I feel that the two complete strangers of a year ago
> are strangers no longer but a part of my life,
> a life in which, if I could do it all over again,
> change all the things that I have done wrong
> I would have no need to change that they are my parents.
> I will always have this anger, this frustration inside of me.
> Each week that goes by our relationship changes, becomes
>   stronger, little by little. It will take a little time but that's
>   okay
> Things change, accidents happen making a lifetime not
>   time enough
> to get to know my parents

You just have to try to forget the lost time. It is very hard, but it's something that needs to be talked about. It may be sensitive for some kids in similar situations because they feel it's their fault but it's not. It's just one of those things that life throws at you and what doesn't hurt you only seems to makes you stronger.

My parents play a big part in my life. They help me out in so many ways. I may never be really close to them but I am glad to have them and am very grateful. We do family things together, like just last week we drove down to Ogden, Utah, to see my mom's dad and mom. On the way there we slept mostly but when we all were awake together it was fun some of the time.

When we got there the adults started to talk, and I heard stories about my mom and dad that made me think I am not much different than they were at my age and that parents are the best thing when you are young and oblivious to the world's ways.

There's no way to pick our parents ahead of the time, before we are born, but one thing life can't change is that family is forever once a bond is formed and becomes strong. Family is one of the most important things in life. I couldn't live without family because they are always there for you and care about you no matter what you do or who you are.

It has been a little more than a year now and I still don't know what exactly I am doing living with my parents. We laugh, we cry, and we share the time that we now have together, making memories that I know I will never forget and ones I know I will want to forget. But getting the chance to know my parents has been the best thing that has happened so far in my life. There is no doubt in my mind that if I could go back and change my life, I would have done it sooner.

*Fifteen-year-old **Amanda Weinert's** goal is to be an OB/GYN and own her own ranch. Until then you can find her riding horses, playing her flute and guitar, listening to music, and writing poems. Her parents inspire her, and she has this to say: "What I like most about myself is my ability to hide my fears from others."*

A LOT OF **JERKS** PLAY **ONLINE** AND I WAS **WORRIED** THAT THEY WOULD **TARGET** MY COUSIN BECAUSE **SHE WAS NEW** TO THE **GAME** AND WOULD **NOT ACT** THE WAY **THEY** DO. I, ON THE **OTHER** HAND, KNOW **HOW TO HANDLE THEM** BECAUSE I'VE **BEEN ONLINE** MORE THAN MY **COUSIN.** BUT **MOST OF THE TIME** THERE ARE SOME **GOOD PEOPLE** OUT THERE WHO ARE JUST **LOOKING** FOR A **GOOD GAME** SO I **RELAXED** A LITTLE BIT.

-MATTHEW VINZON

THE GAMER AND
THE ANIME LOVER

Matthew Vinzon

Nikki is my younger cousin. I am four years older than she is. She is twelve years old and lives in California. She has medium-length hair and wears glasses. The thing we like to do together most is play video games. We have different taste when it comes to games but we like to play Halo together. Because I am the one who has the game, I have to walk her through the basics. I also help her with other games. Besides games, we also share a passion for anime. When we are not playing games we talk about and/or watch anime. We also brainstorm together about anything that we can think of.

I remember when Nikki wanted to learn how to play Halo 2. At first I tried to teach her the basics of the game by playing multiplayer games—things like movement, aiming, and which button does what. I began showing her the different types of weapons. While showing her the rocket launcher I began to talk about the lock on feature and she said "Lock on?" I retrieved the rocket launcher and gave it to Nikki, then jumped my character into a vehicle. After explaining how to lock on to a vehicle, I let her try it out on me. She locked on to me while I was driving erratically and launched a rocket at me. It missed. Then it came around and took out the car. I was in a state of "aww," with my jaw open like I just saw something extraordinary because that rarely happens. Apparently the rocket U-turned, missing everything that would have set it off, and came back. She said, "Is that a good thing?" Yes, that was a good thing. After I taught her how to use a few common weapons, we faced off. I used it to see if she was ready to play over the Internet, which is filled with lots of strong players. Although she had a good hold over the basics, she was not as strong as I was, but she did better than I had expected.

Before we decided to go online, I thought it would be a good idea to play co-op mode so that she could get some practice. Co-op mode is where two players can play through the story mode of the game together, so long as they're playing on the same system together. After I gave her a brief history of the prequel, we loaded up the first level and started to play. The story of the game is basically that mankind has finally become capable of colonizing planets and traveling through space. One day, one of the outer colonies makes contact with an alien ship and tries to communicate with the vessel. Contact with the colony is lost and we find out that a group of alien races is responsible for the destruction of the colony and that they have deemed that humanity is not worthy to exist. The aliens begin to destroy the colonies and they are now on our home planet, which has become the only place for mankind. The main character is a super-soldier who has become mankind's only hope for salvation against this seemingly unstoppable alien Covenant.

After playing through the entire game, we started to play online. Online play is where you can play games with other people over the Internet no matter how far away they are. Playing online is different than playing offline because you can remain anonymous. A lot of jerks play online and I was worried that they would target my cousin because she was new to the game and would not act the way they do. I, on the other hand, know how to handle them because I've been online more than my cousin. But most of the time there are some good people out there who are just looking for a good game so I relaxed a little bit.

After we entered the lobby, which is where you go to choose a game type to play in, like team games or free-for-all games, we chose to go into one of the team matches so that I could help her out if she got stuck in a situation we did not cover in multiplayer. Sure enough, she ran into one. The game had tanks and I had forgotten to teach her how to deal with them or how to drive one. She did not do so well against the tanks in that game. I couldn't help her out at the time because I was faced with my own problem known as snipers. The general tone of the game was frustrating because Nikki was performing badly against the tanks and I was pinned down on the other side of the map so I could not help her. That was the only game we played that went as badly as it did but she did well when she wasn't faced with the tanks. I was amazed at how fast she learned how to play.

Although Nikki and I share a passion for games and anime, she likes anime as much as I like games. Our taste in anime also differs as I like anime for an older audience and she likes anime for a younger audience. However, we do like some of the same shows but she is more up-to-date on the plotlines because she can watch more anime shows than I because I don't have as much freedom with the TV as she does. Although she watches a lot of anime, she sometimes has difficulties understanding certain points of the plots and she will come to me for help. I will walk her through what she is having problems understanding and then I will explain to her what it could mean. After I clear things up for her, her reaction will change from confused to understanding.

Nikki is both family and a friend to me. Most of my friends have moved and to add to that I recently moved to a new city. I also live in a city where the only family I have is my parents but our relationship is on the fringes of exploding in verbal rage. Nikki is pretty much the person in the world that I feel the closest to. Even though we live in different states, we stay in contact by using the telephone, e-mail, and/or IM, which is short for instant messaging. She is also the only person that I can open up to about anything.

She also opens up to me in the same way and sometimes asks for help with her own problems. No one in the world is quite like her.

*Sixteen-year-old **Matthew Vinzon** thinks you should know that he "likes things that don't make sense." But his inspirations make sense: people who are wise or who write, create games, manga, anime or movies – all things he hopes to pursue himself. He enjoyed the 826 Seattle project because "I got some ideas on how to become a better writer."*

MAYBE, EVEN IF YOU DON'T BELIEVE IN EVOLUTION ON THE LEVEL OF PHYSICAL MUTATION, HUMANITY EVOLVES. FAMILY ISN'T WHAT IT USED TO BE.

-SEAN SANCHEZ

...Lost

Sean Sanchez

Traditionally family is the man, the woman, their offspring, and that unit's blood connection to others. Throughout history people have had three generations living in one household, where each generation and gender serves a specific purpose, to help the new generation prosper while maintaining well-being for each member of that family. But culture changes, society adapts and, if you're an evolutionist, we evolve.

Ever since the major social changes resulting from the equal rights movement, society hasn't been the same for Americans. Women entering the workforce have helped develop our diets, as we are now familiar with fast food for breakfast lunch and dinner. Breaking the barriers between inter-racial relationships has changed our culture dramatically, with children that benefit from each parent's genetic assets. Women initiating divorce proceedings has been much more accepted in our culture, resulting in an increased emotional response from their children. Parents that have decided not to physically discipline their children tend to invert that idea and become submissive, resulting in parental abuse. Overall there has been a change in the family structure and the roles for each member. Maybe, even if you don't believe in evolution on the level of physical mutation, humanity EVOLVES. Family isn't what it used to be.

* * *

My family has gone through its share of tragedy, but there has always been good to outweigh any damage done. My parents prove that nothing is black or white, nor is it always gray, it's just what it is, as it is, when it happens.

My father has been a "responsibleish" parent and a loving parent. He's raised me most of my life but always kept his guardianship loose, never waking me up for school, never imposing his will, never keeping a quota, curfew, or allowance for me, always saying, "If you want to do it it'll come from your heart." And that attitude of his applies to anything from college to taking the trash out; to survive I have to be self-motivated. I guess that method of raising a child could work, but I never take out the trash until asked.

My mother, on the other hand, has been recently institutionalized and will not be released anytime soon. Before that, she wasn't a big influence, but yet she was. She was nice, yet unfair. Her and I have had spastic moments, where one second she'd be yelling and I'd be crying my eyes out, then the next second she'd have me pinned to the ground crying from laughter as she tickled me. I never understood her methods until we later realized that she was mentally ill.

The outcome of my parents' relationship to each other and their guardianship has put me in many awkward positions. I've always had issues with women; I'm not sure why, maybe because of my mother, or my dad's involvement in the escort business, and having escort girls that took my dad's attention away from me. My mother and father weren't married, so there was split custody over me, which always made me look like a brat when it came to switching parents for the weekend. Can you blame me? I wasn't trying to make it harder on them, but I did make it hard. There has been a lot of bullshit drama between my parents and my mother's parents that I've never cared about. It was always something like: one person did this vanity drug, the other did that non-prescribed drug, and they don't know how to raise a child; your father did this and that and almost killed the both of us; or, your mother left you at this age and her parents left her at that age, and so on.

My family memories are so serene and eventful and horrible, it's almost surreal. There's a lot to learn over the years from them, whether good or bad. I feel sorry for all of them, but I'm firm in my belief that they're all capable human beings that can get themselves together, and if they can't, I don't care, it's not my problem. I'm going to lead my own life one day, one that'll be away from those silly people that mean to do good but never do.

Besides, family is much more than my parents.

Baseball in the Street

Most of my younger years I didn't have many friends, I didn't socialize with many people my age and there wasn't much past the house (besides my cousins). Then when I came to the age where one runs about destroying things, I did just that. I lived on Henderson Street, on the south side of South Park just a couple blocks away from the freeway, which was well tucked behind the industrial complexes, government housing, and tall beautiful green trees that Washington is well known for. Henderson Street was for those who decided to stay separate from the drugs and chaos that surrounded the neighborhood. South Park, aka the "Armpit of Seattle," was about prostitution, crack, high-speed police chases, and drug busts...but I didn't see that stuff much at all, maybe it was my willful ignorance, because I only heard the stories.

"Hey, did you hear about that house by the community center?"
"No, why?"
"There was a huge drug bust, I guess the police found a lot of crack up in that place there. Well, I guess we won't see those Mexicans for a while." Laughter.

That's all the detail I'd get. South Park would remain a separate world for a while. For the time being, Henderson Street was a dream.

The first time I met my friends they were playing a game of baseball out on the street, about six of them, mostly Hispanic, one black and one white. I was scared to ask if I could play, I think I almost even turned back, but what was there to be scared of? I had lost everything. My father had been arrested the month prior, and I had been living with my mother and her husband. The house was under my mother's rule so there wasn't much to get away with except doing chores and watching TV. My dog Chico, my only friend at the time, was being taken care of by a schizophrenic who was also watching over my dad's home. I wasn't allowed to call my father because my mother didn't want me to talk to him. My well-being had been leveled to the ground

I drove myself crazy thinking about how I was going to escape, get a hold of my dad, and go back home. Soon enough I developed an obsessive-compulsive disorder, praying. So there I was, looking at a group of kids having more fun then I'd had in a year. What was I going to do? What I finally did came to me easy as pie; I decided that if I wanted to do something besides sitting inside loathing it all, then I would ask. I stepped up, I boldly asked if I could join in. From there on, it was somewhere between climbing on the back of the ice cream truck every chance we could without getting caught, venturing out into the bad parts of the neighborhood without our parents finding out, and having video game competitions involving every kid on the block. It was everything we did beyond that which made us US.

My friends became my culture. Pretty soon those six friends multiplied into twelve and then those friends into thirty. From that point on there was energy in that neighborhood. To be more poetic and metaphorically correct, we were the "the Olympic torch" of that neighborhood, that neighborhood was us. Even after my dad returned and I went back and lived with him, I still went to South Park to see what was new almost every weekend.

It was the Summer

My friends were Thrashers. We were multicultural punks that were just out to skate everything in sight, except me, I didn't really care about wooden boards too much. Even though I did try, I just couldn't get it, and why the hell do a sport that you can only do when it wasn't raining? It is Seattle we're talking about, so most of the skating would have to hold off until the warmer months. Likewise it was the summer that really made the memories we have together. The feeling of summer is so distinct from all the other seasons that it's easy to remember everything that happened… besides the times when there was booze involved, and even then I can remember some things, like the times when I didn't have any money so I'd just wait for Willie to get drunk off half of his 40 oz and then give the rest to me. I think I saved a lot of money that way.

Definitely summer. The envy-evoking smell of the neighbor's barbeques and the omnipresent sound of lawnmowers and air-planes going overhead. Summer had that dragging feeling to it, like it wasn't going by fast enough, but acquiescing to the dullness sometimes drove me crazy. Its length was hard to admit to. After an hour of soaking up sun by the pool at my stepfather Donnie's house, I'd get the strength to get up and get my ass out to gather up the crew to go do something, which was stupid because the only thing we'd do during the day was sit on Melanie's deck, on the side of the block, kick it at my house, or chill with the West Seattle group of South Park. So I'd be walkin' down the block thinking to myself how I'm gonna spend the hot summer.

The first house I'd pass would be Melanie's; I'd go to see what's up…nothing, just Melanie's brother Malana and Socon playing video games on the couch and eating rice with dry Mama Raman noodles. So I'd cross the street and hike around the small slope up towards Emanuel and Uddies' house near the community garden, but the summer-induced laziness had them too, they were asleep. So I'd head toward my old elementary school, which was plotted right at the top of the hill. I knew I'd only find the smokers there though, if not that then some kids playing basketball. So I'd make my way up just to find Faruk and Josh smoking a blunt and play-ing basketball—like I expected.

I wish I had some sort of device like in Captain Planet or Power Rangers where I could just be like, "LAZY SH*THEAD TEAM UNITE!" Maybe that's a little extreme, I guess a little bull-ox horn could work, but I didn't have one and neither did anyone else, and no, we didn't have cell phones. At least most of us didn't at that time. So I guess I'd be stuck there with Faruk and Josh for an hour or two, and every two minutes I'd have to tell them that I didn't want to smoke, unless I could convince them to go do something somehow. .

It'd go something like this:

Josh: "Well there's this crazy ass guy that lives at the end of the block that I need to buy a twamp (twenty sack) off of."

Faruk: "Yeah that guy is buck (crazy), he pulled a Kaloshnikov 47 out on Josh's white ass. Josh got so scared that he turned another shade of white."

Then we'd laugh. Faruk is a fickle character in the sense that he's never paid for anything that was for anyone else in his life, but he's a good friend, always there to kick it with you when everyone else is doing something, and is always laughing. Ever since I met him he was laughing, I don't even think I've seen a sour face on him once.

Josh, regarding Faruk's comment: "Damn, Faruk, you're blowing it guy."

Faruk, as serious as he could: "What the hell are you talking about, you just said that the guy was crazy!"

Josh, stubbornly: "No I didn't."

"Dude! You're geekin', Josh. Even ask Sean."

"Sean, did I say he was a crazy?"

I would reply just by shrugging my shoulders.

Josh, actually upset: "Well, I was gonna get Sean to ask him but now you're blowing it, Faruk."

"What?! Nah, shut up, you're the one that's blowing it."

Then Faruk would laugh and Josh would get a little more upset. Then finally after they bickered about it a little more I'd be annoyed enough to say something like:

"Calm down guys. Josh, why do you need to buy from him?"

"Because from what I hear that guy has chronic."

It was a good enough reason for me.

"Okay, then I'll ask."

"You sure? This guy pulled a gun out on Josh."

"Yeah, man, what else is there to do? We need a little excitement, right?" and that'd be that.

I would ask, get the stuff, and peace out—and have them pay me in High Gravity OE, the finest of malt liquor. Then I'd go home and stuff that little bottle under my bed for later that night when we'd all go out to invite some bitties over to kick it and drink at the pea patch. And that was that, with vandalizing, night prowling, skating, and playing run away from the cops, dispersed here and there throughout the night.

The Point is that even though this just seems to be average teenage mischief, it has become a part of me and helped me become familiar with the world. Obviously skating and drinking aren't really ways to get around in life, if that is how you interpret the story. It's meant to be merely a highlight of one of thousands of eventful days we've had together, but the fact is we build off of each other even with this trivial jumble of events. See, my family is who and what surrounds me and the events that I can fully understand, in the raw.

* * *

The Tree either prospers, dwindles, or deviates from it's natural upward path. There's never insurance regarding anything in life; there are historical patterns or maybe family records to learn from so that you can find the path not to follow, but there's no guarantee you'll find, learn, or ever have "perfect." As a matter of fact (note that this is coming from a seventeen-year-old) perfect might be the best work of fiction ever created, and for those who disagree, don't count on having a lifetime warranty with it, that's at least what I've learned since I've been here.

The Family Tree is more than blood or the branches shown, always has been. Instead of showing just blood relatives to record our family history, maybe we should include those most influential, whoever that might be. Maybe the most influential person to you is your friend's mom who bought you and your friend alcohol for all the big parties you threw, or it's your uncle who always dropped knowledge, talked about something deep and inspiring, but was always on your level about it. It could be your lover, habibi, ruca, a lover of the same sex, the editor of this book, the writer of this piece, your vatos, your homeboys, your n----s, a pet, your mother, your father, your faith, a band mate, or anything that has the ability to share its, his, or her emotions with you...that's what I think.

"Making it. Absorbing it. Living it." This is how seventeen-year-old **Sean Sanchez** *describes his approach to literature, one of his favorite things. He also enjoys playing music. After one more year of high school, his plans include attending college and studying journalism. He would like to eventually cover the arts.*

My grandma's a **STRONG PERSON** who has **NEVER** been to **JAIL** or **SMOKED** in her **WHOLE LIFE**. She **SMELLS** like White Diamond **PERFUME**, which is a **STRONG SMELL** that makes my **STOMACH HURT**. She has a **SHORT AFRO** and she likes to go to **BINGO**.

- JaQuenna Wilson

My Life, Grandma, and Fried Chicken

JaQuenna Wilson

When I was little, my mom, my two sisters, and I lived with my grandma. My mom had my oldest sister, Tearra, when she was sixteen. When I was about one or two years old my mom was hardly there to take care of me. My cousin La'Quanna lived with us, too, and she took care of me. She potty-trained me, showed me how to tie my shoes, and did my hair all the time. She even showed me how to walk and talk. La'Quanna took care of me until she moved out to go to college.

After La'Quanna moved out, my grandma started to take care of me. She's a strong person who has never been to jail or smoked in her whole life. She smells like White Diamond perfume, which is a strong smell that makes my stomach hurt. She has a short Afro and she likes to go to bingo. She is sixty-five and works for Tulalip

Casino doing housekeeping. I don't like watching action movies with her because she always asks me what's going to happen next and I don't even know. My grandma signed me up for preschool; she took me the first day.

When I was about five my mom had a baby. It was a girl—she named her Memory. In first grade my mom and my three sisters moved out of my grandma's house. I didn't move out with them. I stayed at my grandma's because my cousins lived there and I didn't want to leave them. In 2001 my mom had one more baby girl— her name is Taviyah.

In the third grade I didn't get to go on field trips because I got in trouble a lot. Like this one time I told the teacher that she was stupid. She told me to get out of her class, and I was so mad I threw a chair at her. I yelled at the teacher and threw more things at her. A teacher named Mr. Greer told my grandma that I wouldn't get to go on field trips if I kept getting smart with teachers and staff. When I got home, she told me to sit down so she could talk to me. She said if I talk back to the teacher it will go on my record and I would turn out not successful. The next day I went to school and had a good day.

I was doing well in school until I got to middle school. My attitude changed big time. The teachers were very strict and I didn't like it so I started to talk back to them. I kept getting suspended, so they expelled me and put me in John Marshall. I wish I had remembered what my grandma told me, but I didn't. The summer before seventh grade, she told me not to go to school and talk back to the teachers or I'm going to be living with my mom. I liked living with my grandma because she is a good cook and not as over-protective as my mom. She cooked for me all the time—my favorite is her fried chicken and greens—and she let me go out to movies with friends.

At John Marshall, we just don't have regular time, like school. It's not as much fun. The teachers get on my nerves and I try hard not to cuss them out because I want to leave and transfer to my old school. The teachers are always talking about points! We get points for being on time to class, focusing on our work, communicating effectively, and following directions. If we don't listen they always say, "If you don't do this, I'm going to take away points." There are a certain number of points I need so I can get my percentage up and get out of here. I need to keep the score I have for the next five weeks and then I can move upstairs to the regular school and eventually back to Denny Middle School.

My grandma sold her house so I had to move in with my mom. Living with my mom and four sisters is hard because my sisters and I fight a lot and my mom doesn't really have time for me. For instance, a few months ago, my sisters had a big fight about a new burgundy blanket that my grandma gave to my oldest sister. The second oldest took it and put it on her bed and it turned into a fistfight. I told them it was just a blanket. After my mom broke up the fight, Teaunna went into Tearra's room and they started laughing about the fight and eating spicy Cheetos. They don't stay mad at each other for a long time. I'm hardly ever there at my mom's house—I'm usually at my cousin La'Quanna's house because there aren't as many people there.

A month ago, my grandma got her new house and I sometimes wish I could live with her, but my grandma wants to live on her own now, after helping raise all her ten grandchildren. I understand that, even though I miss eating her fried chicken.

GRANDMA'S FRIED CHICKEN RECIPE
1. Salt and pepper the chicken pieces.
2. Dip the chicken in beaten eggs.
3. Roll the chicken in flour.
4. Roll it in breadcrumbs, any type, but I like the Italian flavored.
5. Deep-fry it in oil. Do not make the oil too hot, and fry the chicken for about 25-30 minutes if boned. If boneless, fry it about 20-25 minutes.

*What words describe thirteen-year-old **JaQuenna Wilson**? "I'm kind of nice, weird, black, laugh a lot, loud, and energetic." Her hobbies include playing basketball and helping her little sisters with homework. Her grandmother inspires her "because she is strong." Her goals are to graduate high school and college. What else should we know about JaQuenna? "I'm one of a kind!"*

EXOTIC BIRDS SING,
TALKING TO EACH OTHER.
THEY FLY OVERHEAD AND I SEE
BEAUTIFUL HUES OF
RED, BLUE, ORANGE, YELLOW,
GREEN, AND GOLD. SOME
HAVE LONG TAILS THAT
CURL AT THE TIP; SOME ARE
SO TINY THEY ARE HARD
TO SEE.

-MARIALUISA MARTINEZ

Between Two Worlds

Marialuisa Martinez

My forehead glistens with beads of sweat. The temperature is a scorching ninety-six degrees. I am on my way home from the market, carrying a bag full of fresh fruits and vegetables to last the rest of the week. As I walk on the dirt road, my skirt caresses my ankles. To my right, I see the river that runs by the house. The water flows smoothly. I watch fish linger in the middle, their top fins gently touching the surface. Exotic birds sing, talking to each other. They fly overhead and I see beautiful hues of red, blue, orange, yellow, green, and gold. Some have long tails that curl at the tip; some are so tiny they are hard to see.

I arrive at the front of our house, which is a rusty mustard color with a white patio. Surrounding the house are tall tropical trees, and a fresh citrus scent floats in the air as I walk slowly toward the house. I see a few trees with big lemons hanging from them, ready to be picked. There is also a small coconut grove a short distance behind the house. My boyfriend opens the door and steps out on the patio. He is wearing his favorite khaki shorts and a soft green T- shirt. His smile is content and relaxed. His eyes are fixed on me as he walks to embrace me. I feel his warm skin and I think, "How wonderful paradise is. This is where I belong."

"WRRROOOOF!" I hear Peaches yell for attention. I blink a few times and look down at her. Her tail wags; she is happy that I have noticed her and pushes her head onto my lap for some scratches. I rest my hand on her head and give her a couple. As I look around my kitchen, I notice a few things that need to be fixed, like the cabinets I have asked Juan to take care of and then asked him again. I hear rain hit the window and I realize that I am still in rainy, chilly Seattle. My mother will be here soon to have lunch and socialize. Within moments I hear the doorbell ring and I answer it.

"Hello, dear! Have you been outside yet? It's just pouring."

I smile and take her coat, hanging it in the closet. I return to the kitchen and put on a pot of water for tea.

"How was your day, Mama?" I ask as I sit down across from her with two mugs.

"It's been fine. I finished a little cleaning at the house. The usual." she says.

The water is ready, so I pour it in the mugs.

"And how about yours?" she asks.

"Right before you came, I was daydreaming of that perfect day in Mexico. Until Peaches brought me back to reality." I have been thinking a lot about Mexico ever since Juan and I talked about possibly living in Colima for a year with his family.

Just as she has told me many times, my mother says, "Maria, you are in the middle of your senior year. You have a lot to do to graduate. And I thought you wanted to go to college as soon as possible to become a paralegal? You need to make a plan for yourself. Honestly, I think it is a great idea for you and Juan to move to Colima. It would be a great experience to live in a different country and see how thing are there. It might teach you something important you can pass on to your own children someday. But for now you need to put your goals first and figure out what is best for you."

My mother and I spend the rest of the afternoon catching up on each other's lives. She leaves around 4:30 p.m. and asks me to call her later.

As night falls, I am sitting on the couch with Peaches, thinking about my mama's visit, when Juan bursts in the front door and yells out my name: "Maria! Maria!" Even though I am sitting right there, he is so excited that he continues, "Where are you? I have something important to tell you!"

I jump up and grab his hands. "What's so important that has you yelling?"

He is wearing the biggest smile I have ever seen. He tells me to sit down and then he starts: "You know how I have been looking for a different job that pays a little more? Well, I found one and it's more than we expected. I got a real job today and I start tomorrow at 8:00 a.m.!"

I can hardly believe it and we laugh and hug. I cook his favorite dinner and we celebrate. That night, he brings up Mexico while we watch a movie in bed. "So now that I have a permanent job and you're almost done with school, maybe we could save enough money to go to Mexico."

I look at him for a minute, then tell him what my mother and I were talking about earlier in the day. "Well," I begin, "first I need to graduate. Remember how I want to go to college and become a paralegal? How are we going to make that work, too?"

He smiles and says, "Let's talk about that another day."

I shake my head and press forward. "Juan, what would I do in Mexico for a year? You know I like to work to keep myself busy. I watched that video your mother sent. Their bathroom is outside. I don't want to have to use the bathroom and take a shower outside! How am I supposed to stay in touch with my family and friends?"

Juan shrugs his shoulders. "Well, you and I could go to the beaches and relax. You can tan all you want in the sun and cool off in the water. You could drink margaritas in coconut shells. Think of all the clothes and jewelry you could get for cheap. I know you love to shop and it wouldn't add up to half as much as it would back here. And there are a lot of hotels around Colima where you could work. You would be perfect for the job because you speak fluent English and your Spanish isn't bad either. Just think Maria, it's only one year or maybe a little less. Maybe just eight months."

I listen to him and then smile. It does sound wonderful. "I guess we'll talk about Mexico another day."

As I think about possibly living in Colima for a year, I realize that I want to explore more of my Mexican heritage. I want to feel and experience how my father and boyfriend and their families lived before coming to America. Maybe I will learn something important or experience something life-changing while in Colima. I can see myself telling my children stories of my time in Mexico, teaching them about their Mexican heritage. I appreciate my time spent here in America and value my experiences, but I am also longing to try something new. I think living in Mexico would satisfy my need for a change in my life. I still haven't made my decision, but when I do, I know it will be the right one for my future. I trust in my heart.

*Eighteen-year-old **Marialuisa Martinez** has a pit bull puppy named Peaches. She enjoys reading, going to beaches, and shopping. Her goal is to have a career as a paralegal. She likes that she is fun and listens to people's problems. She feels "honored to actually be in a book."*

ACKNOWLEDGEMENTS
(AKA THE MAKING OF A BOOK)

THE STUDENTS WHO WROTE THESE PIECES:

Zak Brinlee	Marialuisa Martinez	Rachel V. Hammer
Joseph D. Bryant	Nyeshaya McCoy	Raymond Wilford
David Bullock	Ryan McFadden	Sean Sanchez
Katherine Graves	Brenda McMillin	Matthew Vinzon
Amanda Henritze	Gina Allisce Mickle	Tyson Watson
Tiarra Knox	Schyler Mishra	Amanda Weinert
Roland Kursar	Devonte Parsons	La'Quinta Williams
Erica Nicole Lee	J.R.	Liera Williams
Marisa Lopez	Vincent Robinson	JaQuenna Wilson

DOING ALMOST EVERYTHING UNDER THE TITLE OF
MANAGING EDITOR:
Bill Thorness (with advice from Alvaro Villanueva of 826 Valencia)

THE 826 SEATTLE TUTORS:

Betsy Aaron	Nancy Johnson	Katja Shaye
Sarah Burgess	Matt Kingston	Jennie Shortridge
David Churchill	LeAnne Laux-Bachand	Betsy Snyder
Jennifer Foster	Hana Levay	Bill Thorness
Angela Jane Fountas	Davida Marion	Alex Webb
Marc Greilsamer	Heather Mead	Brad Wilke
Teri Hein	Jeff Olson	
Terrilyn Johnson	Peter Robinson	

GRAPHIC DESIGN AND PRODUCTION:
Julia Littlefield (with advice from Adam Grano of Fantagraphics
Books)

COPYEDITING:
Bethany Jean Clement, Angela Jane Fountas, Jennie Shortridge,
Karen Snelson, Barrie Trinkle

Heavy Lifting at John Marshall and Caring
Enough to Do It:
Audra Gallegos

Organizing the American Indian Heritage
Students:
Camie Olsen and Boo Balkan

Author Photographs:
Carla Leonardi and Bill Thorness

Inspiration and the Foreword:
Sherman Alexie

Having the Audacity to Think We Could Pull This
Off in Our First Year of Operation:
Teri Hein, Executive Director of 826 Seattle

ABOUT 826 SEATTLE

826 Seattle is a nonprofit organization dedicated to supporting students ages 6-18 with their creative and expository writing skills, and to helping teachers inspire their students to write. Our services are structured around our belief that great leaps in learning can happen with one-on-one attention and that strong writing skills are fundamental to future success. With this in mind we provide drop-in tutoring, field trips, after-school workshops, in-school tutoring, help for English language learners, and assistance with student publications. All of our free programs are challenging and enjoyable, and ultimately strengthen each student's power to express ideas effectively, creatively, confidently, and in his or her individual voice.

All donations to 826 Seattle are tax deductible. For more information please visit our web site: www.826seattle.org

826
SEATTLE